CANNABIS CONNOISSEURS

UNOFFICIAL BUDTENDING HANDBOOK

"A GUIDE FOR BOTH SIDES OF THE DISPENSARY COUNTER"

JOSEPH BADOWSKI

DEDICATION

This book is dedicated to my late father who showed me that anything is possible when you keep an open mind towards life.

Thanks, Dad.

Joe

CONTENTS

ACKNOWLEDGMENTS

I would like to express my heartfelt gratitude to the many individuals who have supported my journey so far. Most importantly my family, colleagues and lifelong friends. Their unwavering encouragement, invaluable insights, and support have played a significant role in shaping this work.

To all those who have been there and to the countless others who have contributed to my personal and professional growth, I extend my deepest thanks. This book would not have been possible without your support, guidance, and belief in my abilities. Your contributions have made a lasting impact, and for that, I am truly grateful.

1
INTRODUCTION

Want to learn a thing or two about cannabis in 100 pages or less? Cool, let's dive right in.

First, thank you for purchasing this book and congratulations on continuing your personal pursuit of knowledge. You have not just taken a big step in expanding your understanding of the plant - you have also taken a strong stance in supporting the greater de-stigmatization of cannabis once and for all. All said – cheers to fighting the good fight, mate.

For those who may not know (likely most), my name is Joseph Badowski Jr. Fortunately, I have had the opportunity to spend most of my working career within the realms of alternative medicine.

In the tapestry of my life, cannabis was always an intricate thread, weaving its way through my journey from youthful experimentation to present day. It was a journey marked by discovery, enlightenment, and a profound transformation of perspectives.

The early years were an era of curiosity, a time when the allure of the forbidden enticed many of us. Cannabis, shrouded in mystery and fear, was a daring adventure into the unknown. I, like countless others, succumbed to the tales of potential peril that surrounded it.

Yet, as I traversed the uncharted terrain of cannabis over the years, I embarked on a quest for knowledge that would challenge these misconceptions. My personal encounters with the plant and a relentless pursuit of understanding began to unveil the layers of misinformation that had concealed the true nature of cannabis for far too long.

It soon became evident that cannabis was not the malevolent force it had been portrayed as for decades. It was, in fact, a complex botanical wonder, with a rich history of use and a myriad of therapeutic qualities. As I ventured deeper into this world, I discovered a community of passionate advocates and a treasure trove of scientific research that shattered the myths I had once held onto.

One of the most pivotal moments in my cannabis odyssey was witnessing the suffering of beloved family members. Close relatives were grappling with chronic ailments that could have been alleviated by the very plant society had demonized. Their pain and the prospect of relief offered by cannabis ignited an unquenchable fire within me. It was a profound motivator, propelling me to strive for change, to make cannabis accessible to those in need.

My journey into the cannabis industry began humbly, with a role as a part-time budtender at a local dispensary. This position was my gateway to the heart of the cannabis community, a place where I was not just an observer but now an active participant in the transformation of lives. It was here that I first witnessed the remarkable impact of cannabis on people from all walks of life.

I saw pain melt away into comfort, anxiety dissolve into tranquility, and despair give way to hope. It was a metamorphosis I was privileged to be part of, and it deepened my commitment to advocating for this miraculous plant. The stories of transformation etched themselves into my memory, serving as a reminder of the profound good that cannabis could bring to the world.

Over time, life led me to the corporate world of multi-state cannabis operations. No longer just a bystander, I became a pivotal player in an industry experiencing unprecedented growth and transformation. It was a world of regulation, innovation, and boundless potential. Here, I learned the intricacies of compliance, the intricacies of cultivation, and the nuances of individualized guest care.

However, this vision stretched far beyond the confines of a nine-to-five job. It was a dream to create a space where cannabis could thrive alongside other alternative therapies, where benefits could be harnessed responsibly and ethically. This vision gave birth to CannaSomms, a boutique firm dedicated to providing comprehensive solutions to enterprises, regardless of their size, in the sectors of cannabis and psychedelics.

CannaSomms was not merely my endeavor; it was a collective effort. It brought together a team of industry veterans who shared the same values and aspirations. Together, we took aim to advance these industries with unwavering integrity and purpose. We were united by the belief in the healing potential of these plants and mycelium, their capacity to transform lives, and the promise they held for a brighter future.

As I reflect on the path travelled, it is illuminated by the progress we've collectively achieved. The stigmas that once lingered are dissipating, and their positive impacts are resonating with an ever-expanding audience. The future shines brightly for the sectors of alternative medicine with innovation flourishing, access expanding, and the healing potential reaching even more people in need.

Looking forward, I am eager to witness the continued evolution of this journey we are on together. Each step we take brings us closer to mainstream acceptance, offering hope, relief, and a brighter future for all. As a community, we'll continue to paint an unapologetically positive, profoundly inspiring, and wholly honest picture of cannabis. Together, we'll embrace its boundless potential to heal, transform, and shape the world into a better place.

Now back to the inspiration behind this book - true intrigue came when I realized the level of restriction, misinformation and flat-out falsehoods that surrounded these medicines of wonder – particularly that of cannabis. Whether it was due to fear or ignorance, people shied away from the plant where it lost it's place in the world as a helpful tool for wellness & spirituality. My hope is to share some of the learned experiences, specifically from the cannabis industry, so that you may find benefit in the forthcoming material that translates to the real world in one way or another. Consider this a sort of personal journal of the topic intended for others to build upon over time.

The primary purpose of this book is to fill a vastly growing void. The void of basic education that can help folks, entry level, executive or regular guest, in elevating their understanding of cannabis - as well as their careers if they happen to relate. This book is not intended to be the "end-all-be-all" of cannabis or dispensary themed books. Rather, it should be continually built upon as the industry evolves so that we may get ahead of the educational curve that we have been behind for far too long. Nothing in here is claimed to be newfound information or personal discovery. It is a simple collection of data, insights and advice passed along with positive intent.

To clarify, this is not some claim to be an almighty cannabis guru who knows it all. I have a hard time even believing that I can be considered semi-knowledgeable on the topic. However, after spending years of making cannabis the focal point of my work and research, there has been one clear trend – tons of people entering the industry with little to no knowledge on the subject. Some, honest and eager to learn, enter to act as sponges soaking up as much information as possible. Others "fake it until they make it", which can be dangerous at times, and go by the seat of their pants. Surely less than ideal regardless of the individual situation.

In both cases, it is typically no fault of the delivering party. Rather, it reflects a much larger and systemic problem surrounding the legality and access to information surrounding cannabis. It went from worldwide acceptance to being deemed a product of the devil during the "Reefer Madness" era, we were told to *"**Just Say No!**"* and then it was kept in a legal vacuum for years to come – let's not get started on the *D.A.R.E* initiatives. Essentially, those with the most intricate access to the plant usually remained on the fringes of society and/or operated within the black market.

All this canna-insanity adds up to the topic at hand: a massive void of baseline cannabis information intended for the public to utilize as this emerging industry continues to go mainstream. Whether you are entering a dispensary as a new guest or day-1 employee, you will now be armed with the information that many of us unfortunately did not have when we first entered the wild west of legal cannabis.

For those who came in its earliest stages, we came bright-eyed & bushy-tailed. Eager and excited for these new legal operators to fill our hands with learning material on the hot topic of regulated cannabis. Finally, we were in a place where we could get the details and information we always wanted to know. What we did not anticipate were these people turning to online search engines to source this information or to answer our questions. Experts, huh?

Gone are the days of cluelessly relying on such methods of guesswork. Say hello to a comprehensive, yet pocket-sized, resource that will equip you with everything you need to know about legal cannabis and dispensaries from a starter standpoint. *"Cannabis Connoisseurs"*, is a book that will empower you to make confident suggestions or purchasing decisions in cannabis regardless of past education on the topic. This will not be a two-thousand page colligate textbook or a satirical take on the subject. It will be digestible, relatable and most importantly – educational. This is a collective of information sourced from within the industry and put into one convenient place for all to enjoy. Moreover, this book is intended to be a bite-sized beacon of knowledge, empowering those on both sides of the dispensary counter to confidently explore the world of cannabis together.

Get comfortable, keep your stash handy & enjoy!
-Joe

2
CANNABIS 101 (SORT OF)

Before we get into the nitty-gritty of what makes cannabis so special and how it's various components may help us over time, let's zoom out a bit – actually a whole lot. All the way back to the most remote corners of the earth during ancient times where we will find the earliest traces of cannabis use among humans. What this illustrates is that cannabis has been utilized for its benefits for far longer than we can even imagine. From ancient Chinese farmers making hemp textiles, Egyptian pharaohs being buried with their stash and Native Americans passing the peace pipe – cannabis has stretched the millennia in being recognized as a wellness tool for societies across the globe.

Our journey begins in the mists of antiquity, where the earliest traces of cannabis cultivation date back thousands of years. Picture yourself wandering through the lush gardens of ancient China, where cannabis was cultivated as a profound source of fiber and medicine. The ancient Chinese knew a thing or two about the herb, utilizing it for its therapeutic benefits and even incorporating it into their religious ceremonies.

In ancient China, cannabis, known as *"ma"* or *"má"*, played a significant role in various aspects of life. The plant was cultivated for its sturdy fibers, which were used to make ropes, textiles, and even early versions of paper. The Chinese people recognized the durability of cannabis fibers and valued them for their strength and versatility over other materials used to make the same. These fibers became crucial materials for constructing clothing, shoes, and sometimes armor.

However, it was the medicinal properties of cannabis that truly captivated the ancient Chinese. Cannabis was regarded as one of the fifty fundamental herbs in traditional Chinese medicine, known as the *"materia medica."* This Chinese pharmacopeia, dating back to around 2737 BCE, documented the therapeutic applications of cannabis. It was used to treat a wide range of ailments, including pain, inflammation, rheumatism, digestive disorders, and gynecological issues. Sounds very familiar to some modern revelations surrounding the plant, doesn't it?

The mystical aura surrounding cannabis extended beyond its medicinal uses. The ancient Chinese incorporated the herb into their religious and spiritual practices. During religious ceremonies, cannabis was burned as incense to induce a state of heightened consciousness and spiritual connection. It was believed to facilitate communication with deities and ancestors, making it an essential tool for divination and shamanic rituals.

Fast forward a few centuries, and we find ourselves amidst the shifting sands of Egypt in the shadows of the Great Pyramids, a land steeped in ancient history and remarkable cultural practices. While we may not be chasing mummies with Brendan Fraser as portrayed in the Hollywood blockbuster *"The Mummy"*, it is interesting to note that cannabis, known for its potential stress-relieving properties, may have been of benefit in such a high-stakes adventure. However, beyond cinematic tales, we have discovered that the ancient Egyptians had a deep appreciation for cannabis and its various uses.

In the grandeur of ancient Egypt, the mighty Pharaohs ruled with divine authority over all who lived there. These powerful rulers were not oblivious to the therapeutic qualities of cannabis; on the contrary, they cherished it for its medicinal properties and integrated it into their daily lives. Historical records reveal that cannabis was employed as a form of herbal medicine, primarily for its analgesic, anti-inflammatory, and sedative effects. It was used as a valuable resource in a time when modern medicine was nonexistent.

Moreover, cannabis also played a significant role in the religious rituals of ancient Egypt just as it did back in China. The Pharaohs, seen as divine beings and intermediaries between gods and humans, believed that cannabis had a sacred quality that allowed them to communicate with the divine realm. They believed that the consumption of cannabis brought them closer to the gods, enabling them to receive higher (no pun intended) wisdom and guidance.

The utilization of cannabis in ancient Egypt goes beyond the Pharaohs themselves. Shamans and healers of the time recognized the potential of this wondrous herb and incorporated it into their practices as well. These spiritual leaders used cannabis as a tool for inducing altered states of consciousness, facilitating visions, and connecting with the spirit world. They too believed that cannabis acted as a portal to the realm of the gods, allowing them to gain profound insights and spiritual enlightenment. It seemed people all over the world were beginning to tap into the wonders that cannabis held.

It is remarkable to observe that throughout history, cannabis has consistently transcended boundaries and found its way into various cultures and societies. From the Pharaohs of ancient Egypt to the shamans of various indigenous tribes, the positive impacts of cannabis on the mind and body could not go unnoticed. The herb's medicinal qualities, spiritual significance, and versatility as a resource have made it a cherished and sought-after plant, continuing to shape human existence across different eras.

But wait, let us take a leap across time and space back to another corner of the globe: India, a land totally steeped in spirituality and enlightenment. Here, cannabis, known as *"ganja,"* has been intricately woven into the very fabric of cultural practices for centuries, leaving an indelible mark on the history and traditions of the subcontinent.

The association of cannabis with spiritual and meditative practices in India dates back thousands of years. The ancient sacred texts of India, known as the Vedas, make numerous references to a plant called *"soma,"* believed by many scholars to be cannabis. Soma was considered a sacred plant, revered for its psychoactive properties and its ability to induce altered states of consciousness.

In India, cannabis was not only consumed in its natural form but also transformed into early-era hashish. Hashish, derived from the resin of the cannabis plant, became popular among spiritual seekers and religious practitioners seeking transcendence and a deeper connection with the divine – likely due to a stronger potency and concentration of THC. What they may have not realized is that they were in fact creating some of the earliest cannabis concentrates found on earth. The methods utilized then to "hand-roll" hash, are still prominently used or referenced when producing modern versions of the concentrate today.

One of the most iconic images associated with cannabis in India is that of the sadhus, the holy men who renounce worldly possessions and dedicate their lives to the pursuit of spiritual enlightenment. Sadhus, adorned with ash and wearing orange robes, often carry a chillum—a traditional smoking pipe. The chillum is filled with a mixture of ganja, tobacco, and other herbs, and when lit, it produces a fragrant cloud of smoke that the sadhus inhale deeply.

For these ascetics, smoking ganja is not merely an act of recreation or intoxication but a means to access higher realms of consciousness and connect with the divine. The rituals surrounding cannabis consumption have deep-rooted significance in their spiritual practices in societies from every corner of the globe. The sadhus believe that ganja helps them transcend the limitations of the physical world and enter a state of heightened awareness, facilitating their meditation and devotion. This is beginning to sound familiar, isn't it?

Furthermore, the cultural significance of cannabis in India can even be seen in festivals and celebrations. One such example is the festival of Holi, also known as the Festival of Colors. During this vibrant event, people gather to celebrate the arrival of spring by smearing each other with colorful powders and spraying water. In some regions, cannabis-infused sweets, known as *"bhang,"* are consumed during Holi. Bhang is made by grinding cannabis leaves and flowers into a paste and mixing it with milk, ghee (clarified butter), and various spices. It is believed to add an extra element of joy and merriment to the festivities.

The influence of cannabis on Indian culture goes far beyond recreational use or spiritual practices. It has been an integral part of the nation's history, intertwined with religious traditions, folk medicine, and cultural celebrations. The rich tapestry of India's relationship with cannabis showcases the enduring connection between humans and this ancient plant, offering insights into the diverse ways in which it has shaped and continues to shape societies around the world.

As we journey further through time, we witness cannabis traversing the globe, leaving its indelible mark on various cultures and societies. The history of cannabis stretches back thousands of years, and its influence can be found in diverse regions throughout the world.

Another significant historical example of cannabis's impact is its arrival on the shores of Africa. Cannabis, known as *"dagga"* or *"ganja"* in different African regions, has a long history on the continent. Indigenous African communities recognized its medicinal properties and integrated it into their healing practices just as other cultures have. Indigenous communities were well aware of the medicinal properties of cannabis and revered its therapeutic potential. They integrated it into their healing practices, like how cannabis was utilized in other ancient cultures around the world. Cannabis, as you can see, has ties to spirituality in every aspect and culture of humanity.

Moreover, cannabis cultivation was practiced by numerous African communities, particularly in regions with favorable climatic conditions. Traditional cultivation methods involved selecting and propagating indigenous landrace cultivars that were well adapted to the local environment. These landrace cultivars, characterized by their unique genetic profiles and distinct regional traits, contributed to the rich biodiversity of African cannabis. We owe much credit to these ancient propagators of the herb for some of today's most sought-after cannabis flower can be traced back to the landrace cultivars of the old world.

The Americas also have a rich history with cannabis before we demonized it into oblivion for a while. Indigenous tribes in North and South America embraced cannabis as a sacred plant and incorporated it into their spiritual rituals. For example, the Native American tribes of the Great Plains region used *"chanupa"* or *"peace pipes"* during their ceremonies, which often involved smoking a mixture of tobacco and cannabis. These rituals were seen as a means to connect with the deeper spiritual realm, seek guidance, and promote peace and harmony within the community. Here too, cannabis  was considered a sacred and powerful plant, capable of bridging the gap between the physical and spiritual worlds.

Cannabis's influence extends even to ancient Mesopotamia, the cradle of civilization. In present-day Iraq and Iran, evidence suggests that cannabis was used by the ancient Sumerians for both medicinal and religious purposes, much like many other nations throughout history. The Sumerians, who inhabited this region around 3000 BCE, held a deep reverence for the plant, referring to it as *"qunubu"* and incorporating it into various aspects of their culture.

The Sumerians, known for their advancements in writing, agriculture, and trade, had a rich spiritual and religious tradition. Cannabis played a significant role in their religious ceremonies too, where it was believed to facilitate communication with the divine and induce altered states of consciousness. It was regarded as a sacred plant, often associated with their goddess of fertility and war, Inanna.

Historical texts and cuneiform tablets discovered in ancient Sumerian sites provide valuable insights into their use of cannabis. These writings reveal that the Sumerians brewed cannabis-infused beverages and used them during religious rituals due to their psychoactive properties.

The Sumerians' knowledge and use of cannabis extended to cultivation as well. They cultivated the plant for its medicinal and religious purposes, taking advantage of the fertile lands and advanced agricultural techniques they had developed. The cultivation and utilization of cannabis by the Sumerians demonstrate their understanding of its botanical properties and their ability to harness its potential for their societal and spiritual needs.

The connection between cannabis and the ancient Sumerians offers a deeper and fascinating glimpse into the intertwined relationship between plants, culture, and spirituality. Their reverence for the plant and its incorporation into religious practices highlight the deep-rooted mysticism surrounding cannabis throughout time.

Throughout history, cannabis has been a constant companion on humanity's tumultuous journey. Its ability to elevate consciousness and provide a sense of well-being has made it a cherished and revered plant in countless societies until we went ahead and messed everything up.

Now, let's delve deeper into the not-so-distant past of modern America, specifically the mid-20th century—a time marked by significant societal transformations, cultural revolutions, and the notorious era of prohibition. It is within this tumultuous period that our tale takes a dark turn, as cannabis, once cherished and widely used, became the victim of political maneuverings, moral panic, and a wave of misinformation that fueled the chaos of reefer madness.

The early 1900s witnessed a growing sentiment of fear and unease regarding the use of certain substances, including cannabis. Influential figures and organizations, such as Harry Anslinger, the first commissioner of the Federal Bureau of Narcotics, embarked on a crusade against cannabis, stoking moral panic and spreading misinformation about its effects. Anslinger's efforts were particularly driven by racially biased narratives, associating cannabis with Mexican immigrants and African Americans, thereby using racial prejudices to further demonize the plant.

In 1937, the Marihuana Tax Act was passed in the United States, effectively criminalizing the possession and distribution of cannabis. The act imposed heavy taxes and regulations that made it nearly impossible for legal trade to occur. This legislation marked the beginning of a new era of prohibition, characterized by a fervent campaign to eradicate cannabis from society. Propaganda films, such as *"Reefer Madness,"* depicted cannabis as a dangerous substance capable of leading individuals down a path of madness and moral degradation. Give this one a watch if you ever need some comedic relief or a good laugh. If nothing else, it will illustrate how far we have come as a society in re-recognizing this plant for its positive potential and overall benefits.

As a result of these ridiculous political and social pressures, cannabis was unjustly cast as the devil's lettuce and banished to the shadows. The mere association with this demonized plant could lead to individuals being cast out from mainstream society or, worse yet, unjustly incarcerated for years or even their entire lives. The consequences of this demonization disproportionately affected marginalized communities, perpetuating systemic injustices that continues to be addressed to this day.

However, despite this dark period, the story of cannabis does not end there. As the 21st century emerged, winds of change began to blow, gradually shifting perceptions and policies surrounding cannabis. The green revolution, fueled by scientific research, changing societal attitudes, and a growing desire for alternative therapies, laid the groundwork for a resurgence of interest in this captivating plant.

Scientific studies conducted over the years have revealed the potential medical benefits of cannabis, prompting a reevaluation of its therapeutic properties. Patients suffering from chronic pain, epilepsy, multiple sclerosis, and other debilitating conditions have reported significant relief through the use of cannabis-based treatments. These findings, along with growing anecdotal evidence, have contributed to a broader acceptance and understanding of the plant's potential.

Moreover, changing societal attitudes have played the most crucial role in reshaping the narrative around cannabis. As public opinion shifted, an increasing number of individuals began to question the validity of past fears and prejudices. Cannabis started to be seen less as a dangerous gateway drug and more as a natural substance with diverse applications, from medicine to recreation. People began to wake up and look past the façade that has been previously created.

This shifting landscape led to the gradual relaxation of cannabis laws in various states and countries. Starting in the late 1990s with the passage of medical cannabis initiatives in states like California, a wave of legalization began to sweep across the United States. Colorado and Washington became the first states to fully legalize recreational cannabis for adult use in 2012. Since then, many other states have followed suit, creating a patchwork of differing cannabis policies throughout the country.

The global legalization movement gained further momentum as countries like Uruguay, Canada, and several European nations enacted legislation to regulate and legalize cannabis to varying degrees. This shift has sparked a significant economic boom, creating job opportunities, generating tax revenue, and stimulating innovation within the cannabis industry. We are effectively in the post-prohibition days and are writing the book on what comes next. It is up to all of us to maintain the momentum and keep cannabis out of the shadows once and for all.

Today, we find ourselves on the cusp of a new era—a time when cannabis is shedding its tarnished reputation and reclaiming its rightful place in society. As legalization continues to gain traction, cannabis is no longer merely a symbol of taboo rebellion but a topic of discussion, exploration, and untapped opportunity. The stigma that plagued this plant for decades is gradually dissipating, giving way to a more nuanced understanding of its potential benefits and responsible use.

In the chapters that follow, we will delve deeper into the diverse facets of cannabis, from its chemical compounds to its various cultivars and even consumption methods. We will also explore and attempt to demystify some of the nuances that surround the world of modern-day legal cannabis. All intended to help a greater amount of people respect and understand the complexities that come along with such an interesting plant.

3
RELAX, IT'S JUST CANNABIS

"I learned a long time ago that reality was much weirder than anyone's imagination."

-Hunter S. Thompson

This chapter is for those who may still have a tad of "Reefer Madness" stuck in their brains or for whom may still be fearful of approaching the topic after years of misinformation being spoon-fed their way. We are here to take a little breather and help dispel any lingering reservations or apprehensions felt towards this remarkable plant. We will walk through the great downfall of cannabis's reputation and how the classroom of counterculture was born.

The journey of cannabis from a widely accepted and utilized plant to an unjustly stigmatized substance is a tale of misinformation, fear, and misguided policies. Cannabis, as we previously discussed, has been used for thousands of years for medicinal, spiritual, and recreational purposes across various cultures. However, it was in the early 20th century that the plant's path took a dramatic turn, leading to its prohibition and the subsequent war on drugs in America.

As we discussed, during the 1930s a wave of anti-marijuana sentiment swept across the United States. This sentiment was fueled by a combination of racial and cultural prejudices, political interests, and sensationalized media coverage. The infamous and aforementioned propaganda film "Reefer Madness" depicted cannabis as a dangerous drug that turned its users into deranged & sex-crazed

16

criminals. Such misinformation and exaggerated claims were used to create a climate of fear and justify the prohibition of cannabis. "Educational" films such as this and many others were played for countless classrooms of youth to absorb and widely abide by for the rest of their lives.

The negative perceptions surrounding cannabis reached their peak in the 1980s during the Reagan era. The Reagan administration launched an aggressive campaign against drugs, including cannabis, with Nancy Reagan's iconic slogan, *"Just Say No."* This campaign aimed to instill a true level of fear and discourage drug use through a zero-tolerance approach. The ever-unsuccessful war on drugs escalated further in the 1990s with the emergence of programs like "D.A.R.E." (Drug Abuse Resistance Education). While these initiatives had positive intentions from the start, their approach relied heavily on scare tactics and did little to  educate young people about responsible drug use. Instead, they perpetuated the demonization of cannabis and contributed to the unjust vilification of its users.

For those, myself included, who went through these charades in middle school, it was surely an experience to remember. An officer came in and eventually held up a giant suitcase of "DO NOT TOUCH" items in front of a classroom full of exploratory and mischievous children – you do the math and think about the outcome. No, it was not an instant generation of newfound addicts, but it piqued interest and introduced an entire lineup of substances (and effects) to thousands of kids who otherwise would have continued to worry about who had the best Pokémon cards after school. In short, the outcome was the opposite of desired. These generations who saw the most drug abuse resistance education, were now growing up to be the most medicated and heavily addicted in all of U.S history – contributing to an unfathomable toll of human life due to the overdoses associated with some of these drugs.

On a lighter note, one of the most memorable aspects of the D.A.R.E. era was the onslaught of anti-cannabis commercials that flooded television screens. The *"Above The Influence"* campaign, popular in the 1990s and early 2000s, aimed to dissuade young people from using cannabis by showing the supposed consequences. These commercials often depicted teenagers as melted or deflated (and sometimes talking to their disappointed pets), emphasizing the idea that cannabis use would lead to a loss of control, identity and respect from others. While these ads were intended to be serious, their absurdity and over-the-top visuals often became comical – particularly when watched from an "elevated" lens.

The unjust prohibition of cannabis and the perpetuation of misinformation have had far-reaching consequences, leaving an indelible mark on the lives of countless individuals. The impact of harsh drug policies extends beyond the mere criminalization of cannabis; it has created a cycle of injustice that has disproportionately affected marginalized communities.

Millions of lives have been upended by the enforcement of draconian drug laws. Countless individuals have faced incarceration, sometimes for non-violent offenses related to cannabis possession (for as little as a single joint) or distribution. These individuals, once branded as criminals and the enemy of society, often bear the lifelong burden of a criminal record, which hinders their prospects for employment, housing, and education. This perpetuates a cycle of poverty and marginalization, making it exceedingly difficult to break free from the chains of systemic injustice.

The war on drugs has particularly targeted minority communities, exacerbating existing social and racial inequalities. Decades of discriminatory policing practices have resulted in disproportionately high arrest rates and harsher sentencing for cannabis-related offenses among people of color. This systemic bias has led to the destabilization of families and communities, further entrenching the cycle of poverty and limited opportunities.

Fortunately, in recent years, there has been a growing recognition of the inherent injustices embedded within cannabis prohibition. Many jurisdictions have begun to enact progressive policies aimed at righting the wrongs of the past. Efforts such as decriminalization, expungement of prior convictions, and the implementation of equity programs seek to address the historical disparities and provide pathways for individuals affected by the war on drugs to rebuild their lives.

Additionally, the legalization of cannabis in various regions has opened doors for new economic opportunities, job creation, and tax revenue generation. Some states and countries have implemented social equity provisions that prioritize inclusion and aim to ensure that those who have been disproportionately affected by cannabis prohibition have a fair chance to participate in the legal cannabis industry. These initiatives strive to rectify the imbalances caused by decades of systemic discrimination.

However, while progress has been made, there is still much work to be done. The legacy of cannabis prohibition continues to cast a long shadow, and the harms inflicted on marginalized communities cannot be easily erased. It is crucial to implement comprehensive and holistic policies that not only legalize cannabis but also continue to address the social and economic disparities caused by years of prohibition.

Efforts should be focused on reinvesting in affected communities, providing resources for education and job training, and fostering equitable access to this emerging industry. It is essential to ensure that the benefits of legalization are shared by all, especially those who have been historically marginalized. The fight for cannabis justice goes beyond simply legalizing the plant; it demands dismantling systemic barriers and working towards true equity and social justice.

This shift in public perception and legal recognition stretches outside of American borders, however. Many countries and states are reevaluating their drug policies, recognizing the medicinal benefits of cannabis, and legalizing its use for both medical and recreational purposes. Efforts are being made to undo the damage caused by decades of misinformation and promote a more evidence-based and compassionate approach to drug use and addiction.

With all that said, let us dive into a few of the bigger myths that remain engrained in some and put these silly fears on the shelf. For any continued progress to be made, we must first get past the misinformation and, at times, nonsense that stands in the way.

Common Cannabis Myths

Myth 1: Cannabis is a Gateway Drug

Cannabis has long been associated with the notion of being a gateway drug, but it's important to recognize facts and not outdated mindsets. Scientific research and studies have consistently shown that cannabis itself is not inherently a gateway drug. The concept of a gateway drug implies that using cannabis will inevitably lead to the use of harder, more dangerous substances. However, this idea oversimplifies the complex factors that contribute to substance abuse. The vast majority of individuals who consume cannabis do not progress to using other illicit drugs. In fact, studies have found that most cannabis users do not develop substance abuse issues and lead productive, fulfilling lives. It's crucial to recognize that individual predispositions, social environments, and personal circumstances play significant roles in determining a person's substance use trajectory. By focusing on education, responsible use, and harm reduction strategies, we can promote a more balanced and informed understanding of cannabis, destigmatize its use, and foster a culture of open dialogue surrounding substance use.

Myth 2: Cannabis Will Make Me Hallucinate

Cannabis has long been subject to various myths and misconceptions, and one of the most common is that it will make you hallucinate. However, this claim is largely unfounded and can be dispelled by understanding the scientific effects of cannabis on the human body. While cannabis does contain psychoactive compounds, such as THC (delta-9-tetrahydrocannabinol), that can alter perception and mood, it does not typically induce hallucinations in the same way as psychedelics or hallucinogens. Hallucinations involve perceiving things that are not actually present, such as vivid visual or auditory distortions. Cannabis, on the other hand, primarily affects the endocannabinoid system in the brain, leading to changes in sensory perception, relaxation, and euphoria. The effects of cannabis can vary from person to person, and higher doses may increase the intensity of these experiences, but true hallucinations are not a common outcome. In short, no – those strong brownies you ate did not make you see any rainbows or make you think you were on the moon – you were just acting like a fool.

Myth 3: Cannabis Creates "Lazy Stoners"

The notion that cannabis inevitably turns individuals into "lazy stoners" is a misguided myth that deserves to be dispelled. The outcome of cannabis use is not predetermined, but rather dependent on the individual using it. While some people may experience temporary relaxation or a sense of calmness, it is important to acknowledge that cannabis affects individuals differently. The key lies in responsible and moderate consumption, coupled with self-awareness and understanding of personal limits. Just like with any substance, cannabis should be used in a manner that aligns with one's lifestyle, goals, and overall well-being. By being mindful of dosage, choosing appropriate Cultivars, and using cannabis responsibly, individuals can fully harness its potential benefits while maintaining an active, productive lifestyle. Ultimately, the impact of cannabis use is in the hands of the user, and with a balanced approach, one can debunk the myth of the "lazy stoner" and experience the positive aspects of cannabis. In other words, it is completely up to you whether or not you end up couch-locked for the day with fist-fulls of potato chips.

Myth 4: Cannabis Is Laced

Legal cannabis, when regulated and purchased from reputable sources, is the safest option available for consumers in terms of contaminants such as outside drugs. One of the biggest myths surrounding legal cannabis is that it is dangerous due to potential contamination. However, this is far from the truth. In fact, legal cannabis undergoes rigorous testing and adheres to strict regulations to ensure its safety. There cannot be a speck of dust in licensed products, let alone any mind-altering PCP or LSD left lingering in your bag of green. Licensed producers are required to comply with comprehensive quality control measures that include testing for contaminants such as pesticides, heavy metals, and microbial contaminants. These regulations are put in place to protect consumers and ensure that the cannabis being sold is safe for consumption.

On the other hand, contaminated cannabis is primarily found and produced within the black market, where there are no traces of quality control or any safety regulations in place. Aka "your dude's" weed is likely full of mold, spice (incense), sprays, bugs, hairs or even a combination of the above. The lack of regulation in the illicit market increases the risk of contamination with harmful substances ten-fold. Therefore, it is that we remain educated and purchase cannabis from trusted sources that operate within the legal framework. By doing so, we can confidently enjoy cannabis products that have undergone strict quality control measures, ensuring safety and peace of mind.

Myth 5: Cannabis Causes Cancer

Come on people, are you kidding me??? There is a persistent myth (likely stemming from competitive industries) that cannabis use can lead to cancer. However, numerous studies have indicated that there is no direct causal link between cannabis consumption and cancer development. In fact, several research studies have suggested that cannabinoids found in cannabis, such as THC and CBD, possess anticancer properties and may even have potential therapeutic effects in combating cancer. A comprehensive review published in the Journal of the National Cancer Institute analyzed multiple studies and concluded that cannabis use does not increase the risk of lung, head, or neck cancers. Additionally, a large population-based study conducted in California found no association between cannabis use and the incidence of lung, colorectal, or bladder cancers. Furthermore, a study published in the journal Cancer Epidemiology, Biomarkers & Prevention reported that moderate cannabis use was not associated with an increased risk of lung cancer even in long-term users. It is important to note that smoking cannabis does produce harmful combustion byproducts, similar to smoking tobacco, which may increase the risk of respiratory issues. However, this risk can be mitigated by alternative methods of cannabis consumption, such as vaporization or edibles. Overall, the evidence indicates that cannabis itself does not cause cancer and may even possess certain anti-cancer properties, although more research is needed to fully understand its potential in cancer treatment and prevention.

Myth 6: Cannabis Is Highly Addictive

Cannabis, a widely debated and controversial topic, is often stigmatized as an addictive substance. However, it is essential to dispel the myth that cannabis is inherently addictive. Unlike substances such as opioids or nicotine, cannabis does not produce the same level of physical dependence or chemical addiction. While individuals may not become chemically dependent on cannabis, it is possible for them to develop psychological dependence. This psychological dependence can be likened to the satisfaction one derives from indulging in fast food. Just as some people may crave the taste and experience of fast food, individuals can develop a psychological attachment to the effects of cannabis. It is important, though, to remember that moderation is key. Just as excessive consumption of fast food can lead to health issues, excessive cannabis use can have negative consequences too. It is crucial to approach cannabis use responsibly and be mindful of our choices, as too much of anything, regardless of its addictive potential, can be detrimental in when used in excess or irresponsibly.

Myth 7: **Modern Cannabis Is "Too Potent"**

Ah, the myth of the big & scary "too strong" cannabis. It's a tale often whispered by those who reminisce about the good old days of tie-dye and bell-bottoms. But let's set the record straight, shall we? The notion that modern cannabis is overwhelmingly potent in comparison to its flower-power predecessors is more fiction than fact.

First and foremost, cultivation techniques have come a very long way since the '60s and '70s. Back in the day, cannabis was often grown outdoors, subject to the whims of Mother Nature herself. Farmers had limited control over factors like lighting, nutrients, and genetics. As a result, the quality of the herb varied widely, with some batches resembling nothing more than glorified hay, "brick weed" or dried out easter grass.

Fast forward to the present day, where advancements in indoor cultivation have revolutionized the cannabis industry. Growers now have the ability to carefully control every aspect of the plant's environment, from temperature and humidity to nutrient uptake and light spectrum. This level of precision ensures optimal conditions for the plant to thrive, leading to higher quality and more potent buds.

But here's the kicker: potency doesn't equal danger. The "too strong" narrative has often been weaponized as a fear tactic to perpetuate the stigma surrounding cannabis. In reality, the increased potency of modern cannabis gives consumers more control over their experience. With access to lab testing and precise labeling, individuals can make informed choices about the products they consume, tailoring their dosage and cultivar selection to their preferences. We live in a world where we can now choose our experience rather than take whatever our hookup gives us that week. Whether it's a gentle 12% or more intoxicating upper 20%'s, the freedom in this choice stems from the advancements made in how we grow our cannabis.

So, instead of bemoaning the strength of modern cultivars, let's celebrate the fact that we have such a wide array of high-quality options readily available at our fingertips. We are far past the days of smoking mystery bags of leafy green that left you questioning its origins or even having a paranoid reaction. Today, we have a cornucopia of finely cultivated cannabis, bursting with vibrant colors, exquisite aromas, and a range of nuanced effects.

Let's face it, we should be grateful for the progress that has been made. We've come a long way from the era of "smoking anything we can get," and now we have the luxury of savoring meticulously bred and expertly grown cannabis. So, let's embrace the world of modern ganja and bid farewell to the days of "hay-bail weed." At the end of the day, our taste buds and endocannabinoid systems deserve nothing less than the best.

4
CANNABIS CULTIVARS

We are here to explore the fascinating wonders of cannabis cultivars, or cultivars as most people know them as. Before we begin, proudly remove a pinky finger from the binding of your book and read fancily as we proceed. For you have just graduated from the uninformed realms of "cultivar" nomenclature and can now properly refer to cannabis when speaking to others. From the rich heritage of landrace cultivars to the arts of modern cross-breeding, prepare to learn a thing or two about some of your favorite cannabis varieties and their history.

Section 1: Landrace Cultivars and Their Origins

To truly understand the plethora of cannabis cultivars available today, we must pay homage to their ancestors mentioned back in Chapter 2's history lesson—the landrace cultivars. Landrace cultivars are native to specific geographic regions and have adapted to their environments over centuries, if not millennia. These cultivars evolved naturally, influenced by local climate, soil conditions, and cultural practices.

Imagine traversing the rugged mountains of the Hindu Kush region, where the iconic Kush cultivars originated. These landrace cultivars, such as Afghan Kush and Hindu Kush, have endured harsh climates and arduous growing conditions, resulting in their distinct characteristics. Similarly, the Thai cultivars, hailing from the humid jungles of Thailand, have developed their own unique traits, shaped by the tropical environment in which they thrive. *Who misses Thai-sticks?*

Landrace cultivars are often named after the regions from which they originate. From Durban Poison in South Africa to Malawi Gold in Malawi, these cultivars offer a glimpse into the rich cultural heritage and ancient traditions surrounding some of the cannabis we all know and love today.

Section 2: Modern Cultivation Techniques and Hybridization

As cannabis cultivation progressed and spread across the globe, the desire to enhance specific traits and create new varieties led to the development of modern cultivation techniques. One of the key methods used to achieve this is hybridization—a process that involves crossbreeding different cultivars to combine desirable traits and characteristics. Much like botanists may crossbreed varieties of flowers to produce new, beautiful, results. Or akin to vegetable farmers who make seek to cultivate the best and reddest tomatoes in the country.

In many ways, cannabis cultivation parallels the world of fruit breeding. Just as horticulturists crossbreed different fruit varieties to create new flavors and textures, cannabis breeders employ similar techniques to produce unique cannabis Cultivars. This approach allows breeders to select for specific attributes, such as potency, aroma, or growth characteristics, and create cultivars tailored to meet the preferences of consumers.

For example, consider the popular cultivar Blue Dream. It is the result of crossing the indica cultivar Blueberry with the sativa Haze. This combination resulted in a hybrid cultivar that exhibits both indica and sativa characteristics. Blue Dream is renowned for its uplifting effects, balanced high, and distinct fruity aroma.

Through careful selection and controlled breeding, cannabis breeders have given rise to an astonishing array of hybrids, each with its own unique combination of traits. From the indica-dominant cultivars that induce relaxation and body effects to the uplifting sativas that provide cerebral stimulation, the diversity of modern cannabis cultivars knows no bounds.

Section 3: Exploring Commonly Known Cultivars and Their Effects

Let us now dive into the vast sea of cannabis cultivars, exploring some of the most commonly known cultivars and their effects. It's important to note that individual experiences may vary due to factors such as personal tolerance, dosage, and method of consumption. However, these descriptions serve as a general guide to the characteristics associated with each cultivar.

1. *OG Kush:* This indica-dominant cultivar is celebrated for its potent effects, inducing relaxation, euphoria, and a sense of tranquility. OG Kush is often associated with earthy and citrusy flavors, and its dense buds are coated in resinous trichomes.

2. *Sour Diesel:* A popular sativa-dominant cultivar, Sour Diesel is revered for its energizing and uplifting effects. It is known for its pungent, diesel-like aroma, and its cerebral high can promote creativity and focus.

3. *Girl Scout Cookies (GSC):* GSC is a hybrid cultivar that offers a balance between uplifting and relaxing effects. It combines the genetics of the sativa Durban Poison and the indica OG Kush. GSC is often praised for its sweet and earthy flavors, and its effects can range from euphoria to relaxation.

4. *Jack Herer:* Named after the renowned cannabis activist, Jack Herer is a sativa-dominant cultivar known for its invigorating and uplifting effects. It is cherished for its spicy and herbal flavors, and its cerebral high can enhance creativity and focus.

5. *Northern Lights:* This legendary indica cultivar is cherished for its potent body high and relaxation-inducing effects. It is known for its sweet and spicy aroma and its ability to promote deep relaxation and sleep.

These are just a few examples of the vast array of cannabis cultivars available. Each cultivar offers a unique combination of effects, flavors, and aromas, allowing consumers to find their preferred cannabis experience.

Section 4: The Art of Crossbreeding and Cultivar Creation

The creation of new cannabis cultivars through cross-breeding is an art form that requires skill, patience, and a deep understanding of genetics. Breeders carefully select parent cultivars with desired traits, considering factors such as cannabinoid profiles, terpene profiles, and growth characteristics.

Through controlled pollination, breeders cross the male plants of one cultivar with the female plants of another. This process combines the genetic traits of both parent cultivars, resulting in offspring that inherit characteristics from each.

Selective breeding continues over multiple generations, with breeders meticulously choosing the best progeny to carry forward and refining the desired traits. This iterative process allows for the development of new cannabis cultivars with specific combinations of traits, whether it's heightened potency, unique flavors, or tailored effects.

Much like how fruit breeding has brought us varieties like the Honeycrisp apple or the seedless watermelon, cannabis breeding has given rise to an incredible diversity of cultivars, each with its own distinct qualities.

Section 5: The Future of Cannabis Cultivation

As cannabis continues to gain acceptance and legality in many regions, the world of cultivation is poised for further innovation and exploration. Advances in genetic analysis and breeding techniques hold the promise of creating even more precise and tailored cannabis varieties.

Additionally, the emerging field of cannabis research allows for a deeper understanding of the plant's chemical composition and its potential applications. With increased knowledge, breeders can create cultivars with specific cannabinoid and terpene profiles to target different therapeutic needs.

Furthermore, sustainable and environmentally conscious cultivation practices are gaining traction, mirroring the growing interest in organic and regenerative agriculture. Just as the cultivation of fruits and vegetables is evolving to prioritize sustainability, cannabis cultivation can follow suit by minimizing ecological impact and promoting responsible farming practices.

In conclusion, cannabis cultivars, or cultivars, offer a fascinating journey through time and genetics. From the ancient landrace cultivars rooted in specific regions to the modern hybrids born from the art of cross-breeding, the world of cannabis cultivation is a testament to the ingenuity and creativity of breeders. As we continue to explore the depths of cannabis, we uncover new flavors, effects, and possibilities, expanding our understanding and appreciation for this remarkable plant. So, let us embark on this journey of discovery, embracing the diverse tapestry of cannabis cultivars and the wonders they hold.

Section 6: Reclassifying Cannabis

Contrary to popular belief, no, not all sativas will not make you speedy or paranoid. In the same light, not all indicas will make you sleepy or couch locked. These classifications widely used to define a particular cannabis cultivar have become increasingly dated and unreliable throughout the years.

Cannabis, a remarkable plant known for its therapeutic potential and recreational use, has been classified into three distinct categories for decades: sativa, hybrid, and indica. However, recent advancements in cannabis research have challenged the reliability and relevance of these classifications. Modern studies and scientific evidence have revealed that the full spectrum of cannabinoids and terpenes present within a particular cultivar plays a more significant role in defining the cannabis experience. In other words, we are going to dive deeper into the wonders of this plant so that you may be empowered to understand what you are looking at or being sold when in a dispensary.

The Origins of Sativa, Hybrid, and Indica Classifications

The sativa, hybrid, and indica classifications originated from early taxonomical distinctions made by 18th-century botanists. Sativa plants were originally identified as originating from tropical regions, while indica plants were believed to come from more temperate climates. Hybrids were the result of crossbreeding between sativa and indica cultivars. These classifications were primarily based on physical characteristics such as plant structure, leaf shape, and growth patterns. Outside of general knowledge, they were overlooking the full chemical makeup that defines one cannabis cultivar from the next.

Limitations of Sativa, Hybrid, and Indica Classifications

1. **Inconsistent Effects:** One of the fundamental shortcomings of the sativa, hybrid, and indica classifications is their inability to consistently predict the effects of a particular cultivar. Sativa cultivars were traditionally associated with energizing, uplifting effects, while indica cultivars were considered more relaxing and sedating. However, contemporary research suggests that these effects are not solely determined by the plant's classification but rather the complex interactions between cannabinoids and terpenes.

2. **Genetic Mixing:** Over the years, crossbreeding and genetic

mixing have become widespread within the cannabis industry. As a result, many cultivars available today are hybrids that combine characteristics from various ancestral lineages. This genetic mixing blurs the boundaries between sativa, hybrid, and indica, making it increasingly challenging to rely on these classifications to determine the effects of a specific cultivar.

The Future of Cannabis Classification

As our understanding of cannabis advances, it becomes evident that the sativa, hybrid, and indica classifications are outdated and inadequate for accurately assessing the effects of cannabis. Moving forward, a more comprehensive and precise focus should be taken to consider the full spectrum of cannabinoids and terpenes present within a particular cultivar. This shift allows for a more personalized and tailored experience, catering to individual needs and preferences. Embracing this knowledge paves the way for a new era of personalized cannabis consumption, empowering individuals to make informed choices that suit their needs, while shedding a positive light on the progress we have made in unlocking the potential of this remarkable plant.

5

THE WONDERFUL WORLD OF TERPENES

In the intricate landscape of cannabis, there exists a hidden realm of aromatic compounds known as terpenes. These compounds, found in various plants and responsible for their distinct scents, play a vital role in shaping the cannabis experience. So significant is their influence that we dedicate an entire chapter to unraveling the complexities of terpenes and their impact on the cannabis journey.

When we embark on a cannabis adventure, THC (tetrahydrocannabinol) often takes the spotlight as the primary driver of our experience. After all, it is the psychoactive compound responsible for the euphoric high associated with cannabis consumption. However, understanding terpenes is akin to grasping the essence of the cannabis steering wheel—the guiding force that allows us to navigate the diverse terrain of effects and flavors that each cultivar may hold.

Imagine THC as the gas pedal, propelling us forward with its intoxicating effects. It holds the power to elevate mood, induce relaxation, or spark creativity. However, without the presence of terpenes, we may find ourselves hurtling down the cannabis highway without a means to control our direction or even understand how we ended up there to begin with.

Terpenes, on the other hand, are the much-needed steering wheel in this equation, offering a nuanced approach to our cannabis experience. These aromatic compounds are produced in the resin glands of cannabis plants, alongside cannabinoids like THC and CBD.

They give each cultivar its distinctive scent, ranging from citrusy and fruity to earthy and piney.

But terpenes are not mere fragrance molecules; they have a remarkable synergy with cannabinoids, influencing the effects and therapeutic potential of cannabis. When we consume cannabis, the combination of THC, CBD, and terpenes creates a beautiful symphony that harmonizes through what is known as the *entourage effect*. This phenomenon suggests that the interplay between these compounds can modulate the overall experience, enhancing or modifying the effects in unique ways.

Consider the terpene myrcene, which is commonly found in cannabis cultivars such as Rhythm's famous Brownie Scout and the timeless classic Granddaddy Purple. This terpene possesses sedative properties and is associated with calming effects. Its presence in a cultivar high in THC may result in a more relaxing and soothing experience, promoting restful sleep or deep relaxation.

On the other hand, cultivars rich in limonene, a citrusy terpene found in cultivars like Pineapple Express and Super Lemon OG, may offer uplifting and energizing effects. Limonene has been linked to mood enhancement and stress relief, making it a valuable component for those seeking a more invigorating cannabis experience.

The diverse array of terpenes found in cannabis extends beyond myrcene and limonene, encompassing compounds like pinene, linalool, caryophyllene, and many more. Each terpene contributes its unique set of properties, flavors, and potential therapeutic benefits, enriching the cannabis experience with its nuanced presence. It is worth noting that not all terpenes will impact everyone the same way. We must first listen to our bodies as we experiment with cannabis to understand which terpenes work the best for us, and the reasons why.

By understanding terpenes, we gain the power to curate our cannabis encounters with greater precision. Whether seeking relaxation, focus, or creativity, the knowledge of terpenes empowers us to select cultivars that align with our desired outcomes. No longer will you be guessing or relying on THC percentages alone. We can now confidently select a product and have a strong understanding of the outcome it will bring based on the terpene profile present.

Moreover, terpenes offer not only sensory delights but also potential therapeutic benefits. Research suggests that certain terpenes exhibit anti-inflammatory, analgesic, anxiolytic, and even antibacterial properties – even by themselves or when found in other natural settings. These findings open doors to exploring the medicinal potential of terpenes beyond their olfactory appeal.

In this chapter, we will dive a bit deeper into the wonderful world of terpenes, delving into their individual characteristics, potential effects, and the cultivars where they commonly reside. We unravel the secrets behind the scents and unveil the significance of these aromatic compounds in shaping the cannabis landscape.

For with each inhalation, we enter a world where THC and terpenes dance in harmony, guiding our experience and steering us towards new realms of possibility.

Limonene

A terpene commonly found in citrus fruits and, of course, certain cannabis cultivars, is a shining star in the aromatic symphony of cannabis. With its vibrant and zesty aroma reminiscent of freshly squeezed lemons, limonene brings a burst of sunshine to the cannabis experience. Not only does it delight the senses, but it also holds potential therapeutic properties that make it a sought-after component.

Limonene has been associated with mood enhancement, stress relief, and a general sense of upliftment. Just as the scent of a freshly peeled lemon can invigorate and awaken the senses, limonene-infused cultivars, such as Lemon Haze or Super Lemon OG, have the power to elevate mood and instill a sunny disposition. Its uplifting effects can promote a sense of positivity, making it an ideal choice for those seeking a more energizing and cheerful cannabis experience.

Beyond its aromatic charm, limonene has caught the attention of researchers exploring its potential health benefits. Preliminary studies suggest that limonene exhibits anti-inflammatory and antioxidant properties, which may contribute to its therapeutic potential. It has also shown promise as a possible treatment for anxiety and depression, with its mood-enhancing effects providing a ray of hope for those in search of natural remedies.

Linalool

Ah, linalool, a terpene close to my heart and a personal favorite for many cannabis connoisseurs. This delightful compound can be found in cultivars such as Lavender Kush and LA Confidential, where its presence imbues the experience with a touch of floral elegance. Linalool, with its soothing and calming properties, offers a gentle embrace, whisking away worries and stress with each inhale. Its enchanting aroma evokes fields of blooming lavender, transporting us to a serene oasis of tranquility. As we indulge in cultivars rich in linalool, we may find ourselves enveloped in a sense of deep relaxation, providing respite from the demands of the day. Its subtle yet significant influence adds a delicate layer of serenity to the cannabis journey, making it a cherished ally for those seeking moments of peace and unwinding. So, let linalool's aromatic embrace transport you to a world of calm and repose, where the worries of the world melt away, and serenity reigns supreme.

Myrcene

My second favorite, a terpene of intrigue and ever so much allure. Found abundantly in certain cannabis cultivars, this aromatic compound holds the power to transport us to a realm of tranquility and relaxation. With its earthy, musky aroma reminiscent of cloves and hops, myrcene captivates the senses and whispers promises of serenity.

Known for its sedative properties, myrcene is often associated with soothing effects, making it a beloved component for those seeking a calm and restful cannabis experience. This terpene, with its comforting embrace, can ease the mind and body, melting away tension and inviting a sense of deep relaxation.

But myrcene's influence extends beyond its ability to induce relaxation. Some believe that it plays a crucial role in the entourage effect, amplifying the therapeutic potential of other cannabinoids present in the cultivar. As a prominent terpene in indica-dominant varieties, myrcene is often praised for its potential analgesic properties, providing relief from discomfort and promoting a sense of physical ease.

Furthermore, myrcene's presence in cannabis can influence the overall effects of the cultivar. When combined with higher levels of THC, it may enhance the sedative qualities and deepen the calming experience. Imagine sinking into a plush armchair, enveloped in a gentle haze of tranquility, as myrcene whispers sweet lullabies to your senses.

So, when encountering a cultivar with a pronounced myrcene profile, you can typically prepare yourself for a journey of relaxation, as this terpene weaves its magic and guides you to a tranquil state of being. Embrace the soothing embrace of myrcene, and allow yourself to be transported to a realm where worries fade and serenity takes hold.

Caryophyllene

Enter the enigmatic world of caryophyllene, a terpene that adds its own distinct flavor and therapeutic potential to the cannabis experience. Found in various cultivars, caryophyllene captivates our senses with its unique spicy and peppery aroma. There are two forms of caryophyllene: alpha-caryophyllene and beta-caryophyllene.

Alpha-caryophyllene, also known as humulene, not only contributes to the earthy and woody scent of some cannabis cultivars but also boasts potential anti-inflammatory properties. This terpene has been the subject of scientific investigation, with studies suggesting that it may exhibit analgesic effects and could potentially support the management of pain and inflammation.

On the other hand, beta-caryophyllene, commonly found in cultivars like Girl Scout Cookies and Skywalker OG, holds its own distinctive characteristics. Notably, it has gained attention for its unique ability to interact with the body's endocannabinoid system by selectively binding to CB2 receptors. This interaction makes beta-caryophyllene the only known terpene that acts as a cannabinoid. By activating CB2 receptors, beta-caryophyllene potentially offers anti-inflammatory and neuroprotective effects, making it a fascinating component in the world of cannabis therapeutics.

The presence of caryophyllene in cannabis cultivars adds depth and complexity to the overall experience. Its spicy and peppery notes can enhance the sensory journey, providing a pleasurable and distinct flavor profile. Moreover, the potential therapeutic benefits associated with caryophyllene contribute to its allure, expanding the possibilities for cannabis as a source of relief and well-being.

As we explore the intricate tapestry of cannabis, caryophyllene stands as a testament to the diverse and fascinating world of terpenes. Its aromatic presence and potential medicinal properties offer yet another layer to the intricate dance between cannabinoids and terpenes, providing further avenues for discovery and understanding in our exploration of this extraordinary plant.

Pinene

A terpene that offers a refreshing and invigorating experience reminiscent of a walk through a lush pine forest. Found in various cannabis cultivars, pinene is a true aromatic powerhouse. There are two primary variations of pinene: alpha-pinene and beta-pinene.

Alpha-pinene, as the name suggests, is the more common form of pinene found in cannabis. Its distinctive scent carries notes of pine and evergreen, evoking a sense of crispness and vitality. This terpene is not only present in cannabis but also abundantly found in other coniferous trees, such as pine and fir. In fact, alpha-pinene is considered one of the most prevalent terpenes in the plant kingdom.

When it comes to effects, alpha-pinene is believed to have potential anti-inflammatory properties. It has been the focus of scientific research exploring its therapeutic potential. Some studies suggest that alpha-pinene may aid in respiratory health by acting as a bronchodilator, potentially opening up airways and facilitating easier breathing. Additionally, it may contribute to improved cognitive function and memory retention.

On the other hand, *beta-pinene* offers its own unique character within the realm of terpenes. Although less abundant in cannabis compared to alpha-pinene, it still leaves a remarkable impact. With its woody and earthy aroma, beta-pinene adds depth to the sensory experience. This terpene can be found not only in cannabis but also in other plants like rosemary, basil, and sage.

Beta-pinene is often associated with its potential anti-inflammatory and analgesic properties. It has been studied for its role in traditional medicine and is believed to exhibit therapeutic effects, including reducing pain and inflammation. Additionally, it may contribute to a sense of relaxation and calmness, allowing for a more serene and balanced cannabis experience.

The presence of pinene, whether in its alpha or beta form, offers cannabis enthusiasts a delightful journey through aromatic landscapes. Cultivars high in pinene can provide a sense of alertness, clarity, and an energizing boost, making them a popular choice for those seeking focus and productivity.

Next time you encounter the scent of fresh pine in your cannabis, remember the magic of pinene. Its presence not only enhances the aroma but also contributes to the intricate tapestry of effects and potential therapeutic benefits that cannabis has to offer. So take a moment to appreciate the allure of pinene as it weaves its aromatic spell, immersing you in the splendor of nature's scents and the wonders of cannabis.

Humulene

Now, let us turn our attention to a particularly intriguing terpene known as humulene. Found not only in cannabis but also in various other plants like hops, cloves, and basil, humulene lends its distinct character to certain cannabis cultivars, adding depth to the aromatic symphony.

Humulene is responsible for the earthy, woody, and slightly spicy notes that often accompany cannabis varieties such as Headband and Skywalker OG. Beyond its aromatic contributions, this terpene holds potential therapeutic benefits that have piqued the interest of researchers.

In addition to its rich scent profile, humulene has been studied for its anti-inflammatory and analgesic properties. Early research suggests that this terpene may help alleviate discomfort and reduce inflammation, making it an intriguing component for those seeking natural remedies.

In traditional medicine practices, humulene has also been associated with appetite-suppressing properties, which may be of interest to individuals looking to manage their food intake. Furthermore, some studies suggest that humulene exhibits antibacterial and antifungal activities, hinting at its potential as a natural defense mechanism in certain cannabis cultivars.

While more research is needed to fully uncover the extent of humulene's therapeutic potential, its presence in cannabis offers a tantalizing glimpse into the intricate interplay between terpenes and cannabinoids.

So, the next time you encounter a cultivar enriched with the enchanting presence of humulene, take a moment to appreciate its unique contribution to the sensory experience. From its alluring aroma to its potential health benefits, humulene adds another layer of complexity to the world of cannabis terpenes, ensuring that each encounter is a journey filled with wonder and exploration.

"A GUIDE FOR BOTH SIDES OF THE DISPENSARY COUNTER"

THC IS YOUR GAS PEDAL, TERPENES ARE YOUR STEERING WHEEL

CANNABIS TERPENES

6

THE ENDOCANNABINOID SYSTEM
&
OTHER IMPACTFUL CANNABINOIDS

In the vast realm of cannabis, we encounter a fascinating and diverse group of compounds known as cannabinoids. These chemical constituents, existing alongside terpenes, weave together to create the intricate tapestry of effects and therapeutic potential that cannabis offers. To truly understand the profound impact of cannabinoids on our cannabis encounters, we must first delve into the intricate system within our bodies that interacts with these compounds – *the endocannabinoid system (ECS).*

The endocannabinoid system is a complex network of receptors, enzymes, and endocannabinoids that exists naturally within every person. Yep, that means we all are born with a natural neurological network fine-tuned for cannabis. It plays a crucial role in maintaining homeostasis, or balance, in our bodies. Discovered in the late 1980s, the ECS has since emerged as a significant physiological system, involved in regulating various processes such as mood, appetite, pain perception, immune function, and more.

The ECS consists of two primary types of receptors: CB1 and CB2. CB1 receptors are predominantly found in the central nervous system, including the brain, while CB2 receptors are mainly located in the immune system and peripheral tissues. Endocannabinoids, the body's own naturally produced cannabinoids, bind to these receptors to initiate various physiological responses.

THE ~~UNOFFICIAL~~ BUDTENDING HANDBOOK

"A GUIDE FOR BOTH SIDES OF THE DISPENSARY COUNTER"

IMPACTS OF THE ENDOCANNABINOID SYSTEM

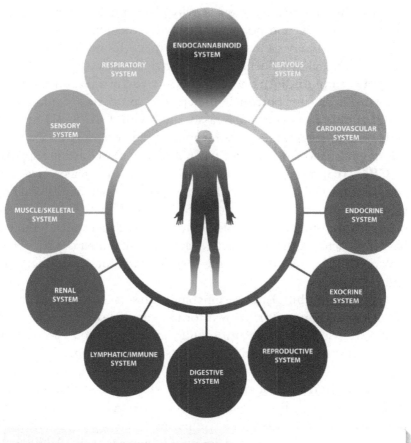

PAIN	MOOD
APPETITE	**ENERGY**
SENSATION	**METABOLISM**
INFLAMMATION	**STRESS RESPONSE**
THERMOREGULATION	MUSCLE CONTROL
EYE OCULAR PRESSURE	MOTIVATION & REWARD

Interestingly, the cannabinoids found within cannabis plants, known as phytocannabinoids, have a striking similarity in structure and function to our endocannabinoids. When we consume cannabis, these phytocannabinoids interact with our ECS, binding to CB1 and CB2 receptors and modulating their activity. This interaction gives rise to the diverse effects and potential therapeutic benefits associated with cannabis use. Every cannabinoid and terpene found within cannabis has the potential to influence the ECS in different ways.

CBD (cannabidiol): one of the most well-known cannabinoids, is cherished for its potential therapeutic properties without the intoxicating effects commonly associated with THC. CBD interacts with various receptors and non-cannabinoid receptors in the body, offering relaxation, discomfort relief, and overall well-being support.

CBG (cannabigerol): although present in smaller quantities compared to THC and CBD, CBG possesses its own unique potential. Often referred to as the "mother cannabinoid," CBG serves as the precursor for other cannabinoids. Early studies suggest that CBG may have antibacterial, neuroprotective, and anti-inflammatory properties, making it an area of growing exploration for researchers and enthusiasts alike.

CBN (cannabinol): is a cannabinoid that forms as THC ages or undergoes oxidation. It is known for its potential sedative effects and is often associated with promoting relaxation and sleep. CBN contributes to the "couch-lock" sensation experienced by some cannabis users, offering a calming and soothing experience.

THCV (tetrahydrocannabivarin): sharing a similar molecular structure to THC, elicits distinct effects. It has gained attention for its potential appetite-suppressing properties, making it an intriguing prospect for those interested in weight management. Additionally, THCV may have neuroprotective properties and is being investigated for its potential impact on conditions like Parkinson's disease.

THCA (tetrahydrocannabinolic acid): serves as the precursor to THC and is found in raw, unheated cannabis. THCA does not possess psychoactive properties like THC but offers its own range of potential benefits. Through decarboxylation, a process that involves the removal of a carboxyl group from THCA, it converts into THC, unlocking the euphoric and intoxicating effects associated with THC consumption.

Decarboxylation occurs naturally when cannabis is smoked, vaporized, or subjected to heat during cooking. It transforms THCA into its psychoactive counterpart, THC. However, decarboxylation is necessary to experience the psychoactive effects of THC, as raw cannabis contains primarily THCA, which does not produce the same intoxicating experience. Therefore, if one wishes to achieve the desired effects of THC, such as getting high, decarboxylation must take place through the application of heat.

As we delve into the world of cannabinoids, it becomes clear that each compound contributes its own unique set of properties and potential benefits. From the therapeutic potential of CBD to the sedative effects of CBN, cannabinoids offer a vast array of possibilities for those seeking diverse cannabis encounters. By interacting with our endocannabinoid system, these compounds hold the potential to modulate our physiological processes and provide a wide range of effects that can be harnessed for therapeutic purposes.

THE ~~UNOFFICIAL~~ BUDTENDING HANDBOOK

"A GUIDE FOR BOTH SIDES OF THE DISPENSARY COUNTER"

NON-PSYCHOACTIVE VS PSYCHOACTIVE CANNABINOIDS

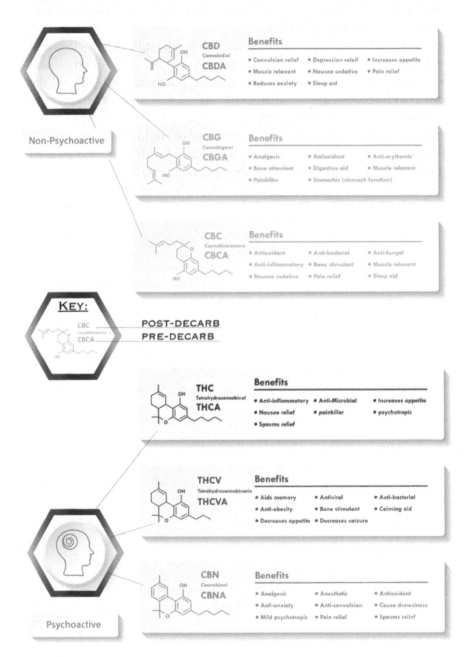

Non-Psychoactive

CBD Cannabidiol
CBDA

Benefits

- Convulsion relief
- Depression relief
- Increases appetite
- Muscle relaxant
- Nausea sedative
- Pain relief
- Reduces anxiety
- Sleep aid

CBG Cannabigerol
CBGA

Benefits

- Analgesic
- Antioxidant
- Anti-erythemic
- Bone stimulant
- Digestive aid
- Muscle relaxant
- Painkiller
- Stomachic (stomach function)

CBC Cannabichromene
CBCA

Benefits

- Antioxidant
- Anti-bacterial
- Anti-fungal
- Anti-inflammatory
- Bone stimulant
- Muscle relaxant
- Nausea sedative
- Pain relief
- Sleep aid

KEY:

CBC — POST-DECARB
CBCA — PRE-DECARB

THC Tetrahydrocannabinal
THCA

Benefits

- Anti-inflammatory
- Anti-Microbial
- Increases appetite
- Nausea relief
- painkiller
- psychotropic
- Spasms relief

THCV Tetrahydrocannabivarin
THCVA

Benefits

- Aids memory
- Antiviral
- Anti-bacterial
- Anti-obesity
- Bone stimulant
- Calming aid
- Decreases appetite
- Decreases seizure

CBN Cannabinol
CBNA

Benefits

- Analgesic
- Anesthetic
- Antioxidant
- Anti-anxiety
- Anti-convulsion
- Cause drowsiness
- Mild psychotropic
- Pain relief
- Spasms relief

Psychoactive

44

7
CANNABIS CULTIVATION

In the previous chapters, we've delved into the components that make cannabis a remarkable plant—its terpenes, cannabinoids, and the intricate dance they perform. Now, let us venture into the world of cultivation, where skilled hands nurture and guide cannabis on its transformative journey from seed to the shelves of dispensaries. Prepare to embark on a fascinating exploration of the cultivation process, unveiling the intricacies and dedication required to bring forth the highest quality cannabis.

1. **Germination** *(The Journey Begins)* It all starts with a seed—a tiny vessel of potential. Cultivators carefully select premium seeds, ensuring genetic stability and desirable traits. These seeds are delicately placed in a germination medium, typically a moist paper towel or a specialized germination cube. Under controlled conditions of warmth, humidity, and darkness, the seeds awaken from their slumber, sprouting delicate taproots that signal the beginning of life.

2. **Seedling Stage** *(Nurturing New Growth)* As the seedlings emerge, they are delicately transplanted into small pots or starter cubes filled with a nutrient-rich soil mix. Tender care is provided, ensuring optimal light, humidity, and temperature levels. The seedlings develop their first set of leaves, reaching for the light with eager determination. During this stage, cultivators closely monitor watering, feeding, and

environmental conditions, providing the necessary support for healthy growth.

3. **Vegetative Stage** *(Green Canopies)* With the seedlings now established, they enter the vegetative stage. Cultivators adjust the lighting to a longer photoperiod, mimicking the longer days of spring or summer. This encourages vigorous growth as the plants develop lush green foliage, thickening stems, and branching out. Nutrient schedules are carefully tailored to provide the essential elements for robust development. Pruning and training techniques may be employed to shape the canopy, promote airflow, and enhance light penetration.

4. **Flowering Stage** *(The Buds Unveiled)* As the plants mature, a critical shift occurs—the transition to the flowering stage. Cultivators adjust the light cycle to mimic the shorter days of autumn, signaling the plants to divert their energy toward bud production. Buds begin to form, swelling and becoming densely packed with trichomes, the resinous glands that house cannabinoids and terpenes. Throughout this stage, cultivators meticulously monitor environmental factors, adjusting humidity, temperature, and nutrient levels to ensure optimal conditions for bud development.

5. **Harvest** *(The Culmination of Cultivation)* When the time is right, the moment of harvest arrives—a culmination of patience, expertise, and precision. Cultivators assess the plants, examining the trichomes under a magnifying glass to determine the ideal harvest window. Once determined, the plants are carefully cut and trimmed, separating the valuable flowers from the leaves and stems. The flowers are then hung in a controlled environment to initiate the drying process.

6. **Drying and Curing** *(Unleashing the Flavors)* During drying and curing, the plants undergo a transformative phase. They are hung in a well-ventilated area with controlled humidity, allowing moisture to slowly evaporate from the flowers. This slow drying process ensures the preservation of delicate terpenes and the development of desirable flavors. After the initial drying, the flowers are carefully stored in airtight containers, and the curing process begins. Over several weeks, the flowers are regularly monitored, burped to release built-up gases, and carefully aged to achieve the desired flavor, aroma,

and smoothness.

7. **Quality Control** *(Ensuring Excellence)* Throughout the cultivation journey, quality control is of paramount importance. Cultivators conduct rigorous testing to monitor cannabinoid and terpene profiles, ensuring compliance with regulatory standards. They also assess the flowers for visual appeal, aroma, and overall quality, ensuring only the finest specimens make it to the dispensary shelves.

8. **Dispensary Arrival** *(The Final Destination)* After passing stringent quality checks, the carefully cultivated and cured flowers or processed products finally reach their destination— the dispensary. Here, budtenders assist guests, showcasing the fruits of the cultivators' labor. With a wealth of knowledge about the cultivars, effects, and characteristics, budtenders guide guests on their cannabis journey, helping them find the perfect match for their preferences and needs.

The cultivation of cannabis is a labor of love, a harmonious collaboration between nature and the skilled hands of cultivators. From the humble seed to the meticulously cured flower, each step in the process requires knowledge, care, and dedication. It is through this commitment that the world of cannabis thrives, offering a diverse array of cultivars and experiences to enrich the lives of enthusiasts and consumers alike.

Disclaimer: The following section is intended for educational purposes only. Before attempting to grow cannabis at home, it is essential to research and understand the local and state laws regarding cultivation. Compliance with applicable laws and regulations is the responsibility of the reader.

Growing cannabis at home can be a rewarding and fulfilling experience. Not only does it provide the opportunity to cultivate your own high-quality cannabis, but it also allows for a deeper understanding of the plant's life cycle and the ability to tailor the cultivation process to your specific preferences. If you're ready to embark on the journey of home growing, here are some basic tips and tricks to help you get started and achieve a successful harvest.

1. **Know the Laws:** Let's repeat in case anyone misread; before beginning any cannabis cultivation project, it is crucial to familiarize yourself with the local and state laws regarding home growing. Understand the limitations, such as the number of plants allowed, cultivation area restrictions, and any licensing requirements. Compliance with the law is essential to ensure a safe and legal cultivation experience.

2. **Plan Your Space:** Assess the available space you have for growing cannabis. Whether you have a dedicated indoor grow room, a greenhouse, or an outdoor garden, understanding your space's limitations will help you choose the appropriate cultivation method and equipment. Consider factors such as lighting, ventilation, temperature control, and access to water sources.

3. **Choose the Right Cultivar(s):** Selecting the right cannabis for your cultivation goals and environmental conditions is crucial. Some cultivars may be more suitable for indoor growing, while others thrive in outdoor environments. Consider factors such as growth characteristics, flowering time, resistance to pests and diseases, and desired effects when choosing what types of cultivars that you wish to grow.

4. **Quality Genetics:** Start with high-quality, legal, cannabis seeds or clones from reputable sources. Good genetics play a significant role in the overall success of your cultivation. Ensure that the seeds or clones you acquire are healthy, viable, and free from pests or diseases.

5. **Provide Adequate Lighting:** If you're growing indoors, proper lighting is crucial for the healthy development of your cannabis plants. Consider using high-intensity discharge (HID) lights, LED lights, or fluorescent lights, depending on your budget and space requirements. Pay attention to light cycles (vegetative stage typically requires 18-24 hours of light, while

the flowering stage benefits from 12 hours of uninterrupted darkness) to mimic natural sunlight patterns and promote optimal growth.

6. **Maintain Proper Ventilation:** Good airflow and ventilation are essential for maintaining healthy plants. Use fans to promote air circulation, prevent mold and mildew, and strengthen the plants' stems. Proper ventilation also helps control temperature and humidity levels, reducing the risk of pests and diseases.

7. **Nutrients and Feeding:** Cannabis plants require a balanced diet of essential nutrients to thrive. Research the specific nutrient requirements during different growth stages (vegetative and flowering) and use organic or synthetic fertilizers accordingly. Monitor pH levels of the soil or nutrient solution to ensure optimal nutrient uptake.

8. **Watering and Drainage:** Overwatering or underwatering can lead to problems such as root rot or nutrient deficiencies. Water your plants when the top inch of the soil feels dry (adjust based on your specific growing medium). Ensure proper drainage to prevent waterlogged roots.

9. **Pest and Disease Prevention:** Regularly inspect your plants for signs of pests, such as spider mites, aphids, or fungus gnats. Implement preventive measures like maintaining cleanliness, using natural pest deterrents, and researching integrated pest management techniques. If a pest or disease issue arises, promptly address it to prevent further damage.

10. **Harvesting and Drying:** Harvest your cannabis plants at the optimal time based on the cultivar's flowering period and desired effects. Monitor the trichomes (small, resinous structures on the flowers) using a magnifying glass or microscope to determine the best time for harvest. After harvesting, dry your buds slowly in a controlled environment with proper airflow and low humidity to preserve their potency and prevent mold.

Remember, home cultivation requires patience, attention to detail, and continuous learning. Don't be discouraged by initial challenges; each grow presents an opportunity to refine your skills and improve your results. Enjoy the process of nurturing your cannabis plants and the satisfaction of harvesting your very own homegrown.

©Joe Badowski 2023

8
COMMON FORM FACTORS

When it comes to cannabis, there is a multitude of form factors available, each offering a unique experience and method of consumption. In this chapter, we will discuss a broad overview of these form factors, exploring their characteristics, recommended tolerances, consumption methods, and onset timings. Whether you're a seasoned enthusiast or a curious newcomer, understanding these form factors will empower you to make informed choices and tailor your cannabis experience to your preferences.

1. **Flower** *(The Classic Choice)* Let's start with the timeless classic—cannabis flower, also known as buds. This is the raw, harvested plant material that is most commonly associated with cannabis. Flower is typically consumed by smoking or vaporizing. The effects onset quickly, usually within minutes, making it a popular choice for those seeking immediate relief or a fast-acting experience. Recommended tolerance levels may vary, but beginners are advised to start with low to moderate doses

and gradually increase as needed.

2. **Pre-Rolls** *(Convenience in a Joint)* For those seeking convenience and simplicity, pre-rolls are a popular option. These are pre-made cannabis joints, ready to be lit and enjoyed. Pre-rolls are a convenient choice for on-the-go consumption or for those who prefer not to roll their own joints. Similar to flower, the effects of pre-rolls onset quickly, making them suitable for immediate relief or social occasions. Tolerance recommendations align with those for flower consumption.

3. **Infused Pre-Rolls** *(Next-Level Pre-Rolls)* These innovative creations combine the pleasure of smoking a joint with the added benefits of cannabinoids and terpenes infused into the flower. Infused pre-rolls offer a heightened experience by incorporating concentrated cannabis extracts, such as oils, shatter, or wax, into the rolling process. This infusion enhances the potency and effects of the pre-roll, allowing for a more tailored and impactful experience. Onset timing for these potent puppies can be expected to be the same as any other joint – instantaneous bliss.

4. **Edibles** *(A Delicious Alternative)* Edibles offer a tasty and discreet way to consume cannabis. These are cannabis-infused food or beverage products, ranging from gummies and chocolates to infused beverages and baked goods. Edibles provide a longer-lasting experience compared to smoking or vaporizing, with effects typically taking longer to onset— ranging from 30 minutes to a couple of hours. It's crucial to start with a low dose and wait for the effects to fully manifest before consuming more. Tolerance recommendations may vary, but beginners are advised to exercise caution and patience.

5. **Concentrates** *(Potency in Small Packages)* Concentrates are highly potent cannabis products that contain concentrated amounts of cannabinoids. Examples include oils, waxes, shatter, and budder. These products are typically consumed by dabbing, vaporizing, or incorporating them into edibles. Due to their high potency, tolerance recommendations are lower for concentrates, and beginners are advised to approach them with caution. The onset of effects varies depending on the consumption method and can range from immediate to a few

minutes.

6. **Tinctures** *(Sublingual Solution)* Tinctures offer a discreet and precise method of cannabis consumption. These are liquid extracts that are usually administered sublingually (under the tongue) using a dropper. Tinctures provide a relatively fast onset of effects, typically within 15-30 minutes. They offer precise dosing control, making them suitable for microdosing or for those who prefer a more measured and predictable experience. Tolerance recommendations align with low to moderate doses for beginners.

7. **Topicals** *(External Relief)* For localized relief without psychoactive effects, topicals are an excellent choice. These are cannabis-infused creams, lotions, balms, or transdermal patches that are applied directly to the skin. Topicals are primarily used for their therapeutic properties, offering relief from pain, inflammation, and skin conditions. As they are not typically absorbed into the bloodstream, they do not produce psychoactive effects. Tolerance recommendations are not applicable for topicals, as they do not induce a psychoactive experience.

8. **Capsules** *(Controlled Dosage)* Capsules provide a convenient and discreet method of consuming cannabis in a pill form. These are oral capsules filled with cannabis oil or powder. Capsules offer a precise and controlled dosage, making them suitable for those who prefer a standardized experience. The effects onset within 30 minutes to an hour, similar to other orally consumed cannabis products. Tolerance recommendations may vary, but beginners are advised to start with low doses and adjust as needed.

9. **Beverages** *(Sip and Enjoy)* Cannabis-infused beverages are an emerging category that offers a refreshing and alternative way to consume cannabis. These beverages come in various forms, including ready-to-drink options and water-soluble cannabis powder that can be mixed with liquids. The effects onset within 15-60 minutes, depending on factors such as metabolism and consumed dosage. Tolerance recommendations align with low to moderate doses for beginners.

As you explore the world of cannabis, remember that each form factor offers its own unique characteristics and considerations. From flower to edibles, concentrates to topicals, the choice is vast and diverse. Consider your desired onset time, preferred method of consumption, and personal tolerance levels when selecting a cannabis form factor. By understanding these factors, you can make informed choices and embark on a cannabis journey tailored to your preferences and needs.

9
STOP CHASING THC!

Now if chasing the almighty THC is your forte, have at it. Destroy your personal tolerance, waste money, and miss the opportunity to experience some truly inspiring cultivars.

This chapter is intended for those who may be innocently confused in thinking that THC is the sole factor determining the direction of a cannabis experience. We are here to discuss how this is simply not the case and shed light on how you may look past THC percentages alone and truly understand the nuances behind this myth. For insight, there have been 12% flowers that hit much harder than 30%, all due to their unique terpene and cannabinoid makeup – not the sheer level of THC alone.

In a world consumed by instant gratification and quick fixes, it's no wonder that the "more is better" mentality has quickly seeped into the realm of retail cannabis. The pursuit of high THC levels has become an obsession for many, with the misconception that stronger THC equates to superior cannabis. However, it's time to break free from this limited perspective and recognize the true essence of cannabis lies in its intricate web of the previously mentioned terpenes, cannabinoids, and their interplay with THC.

Let's take a moment to reflect on a parallel scenario. When you step into a bar or spirit store, do you approach the counter and demand the highest alcohol content available to become as incoherent as humanly possible? Do you seek out the strongest, most potent beverage without considering taste, aroma, or the overall experience it provides? Of

THE UNOFFICIAL BUDTENDING HANDBOOK

course not! Just as the world of spirits offers a plethora of flavors, nuances, and complexities, cannabis holds a similar richness that extends far beyond THC potency. By skipping right to the highest THC, you are missing a world of new cannabis experiences that can benefit you in a greater fashion.

THC, as we've explored, is the primary psychoactive compound in cannabis. It is responsible for the intoxicating effects that many seek. But here's the catch: THC alone does not define the quality or worth of a cannabis experience. It is merely one piece of a much larger and more complex puzzle.

In our exploration of terpenes and cannabinoids, we've uncovered the intricate dance they perform alongside THC. Terpenes contribute aromatic profiles, flavors, and potential therapeutic benefits. Cannabinoids like CBD, CBG, CBN, and THCV each bring their own unique attributes to the table. It is the interplay of these compounds that shapes the spectrum of effects and sensations we experience with cannabis.

Imagine a cultivar with sky-high THC content but lacking in terpenes and other cannabinoids. It may deliver a potent high, but without the presence of complementary compounds, the experience may feel one-dimensional, lacking depth and complexity. On the other hand, a cultivar with a lower THC percentage but abundant in terpenes and other cannabinoids can provide a multifaceted experience, offering a wider range of effects, flavors, and potential therapeutic benefits.

It's time to shift our focus from chasing the highest THC percentages to embracing the full spectrum of cannabis. By fixating solely on THC, we miss out on the opportunity to explore the rich tapestry of flavors, aromas, and nuanced effects that cannabis has to offer. We limit ourselves to a single note in a symphony of possibilities.

Just as a well-crafted cocktail balances various elements to create a harmonious and enjoyable experience, so too does cannabis flourish when all its components come together in harmony. The *entourage effect—the synergistic interaction between terpenes, cannabinoids, and THC*—enhances the overall experience, amplifying the potential benefits and complexities of cannabis consumption.

57

SYNERGISTIC INTERACTIONS BETWEEN TERPENES, CANNABINOIDS, AND THC

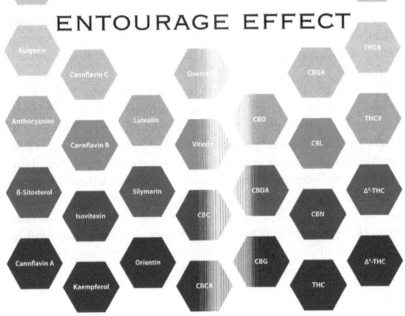

So, let's finally break free from the confines of THC-centric thinking and embrace the beautiful mosaic of cannabis. Seek out cultivars rich in terpenes that resonate with your preferences— whether it's the invigorating citrus notes of limonene or the soothing embrace of linalool. Explore the diverse array of cannabinoids, each offering their own potential benefits and contributions to the entourage effect. It's time to stop acting like an average caveperson by demanding the strongest product in the house – you will be thanked and respected in doing so.

By transcending the narrow confines of THC obsession, we open ourselves up to a world of discovery, where the true magic of cannabis may begin to unfold. Savor the symphony of terpenes and cannabinoids, celebrating the artistry and complexity of this extraordinary plant.

10
ELEVATION VS INEBRIATION

Hey stoney, red-eyed, couch-locked, unproductive buffoon – this one is for you.

In this chapter we will discuss how to completely combat the "stoner stereotype" once and for all. Truth be told, it isn't that difficult and does not require much skill. This boils down to understanding the important differentiation between "Elevation" and "Inebriation". At the core, cannabis should *"ADD TO"* your daily experiences and not *"TAKE YOU AWAY"* from them. Granted, there is always a time & place to over-indulge and melt away but we are here to discuss the latter.

Let's set the record straight from the start. The stoner stereotype perpetuates an image of cannabis users as lazy, unmotivated, and mentally incapacitated individuals who are not capable of much past laughing and overeating. But here's the thing: cannabis consumption does not inherently equate to perpetual couch-lock or a lack of productivity. In fact, many cannabis enthusiasts embrace the concept of "Elevation" rather than succumbing to mindless "Inebriation."

So, what exactly is the difference between Elevation and Inebriation? It all boils down to intention, mindset, and responsible consumption practices. Elevation refers to the intentional use of cannabis to enhance specific aspects of life, such as creativity, focus, relaxation, or introspection. It involves harnessing the plant's potential to elevate our experiences and amplify our senses, much like an artist using a paintbrush to create a masterpiece.

On the other hand, Inebriation is an uncontrolled state of mind that results from excessive or irresponsible cannabis consumption. It leads to impaired cognitive function, lack of motivation, and a disconnection from the present moment. Inebriation occurs when one loses sight of intention and lets cannabis consumption consume them instead – aka you're overcooked.

To combat the stoner stereotype, it's essential to seek elevation and avoid the mindless state of inebriation. Here are some simple keys to help keep your eyes open while partaking:

1. **Set Intentions:** Before consuming cannabis, take a moment to reflect on your goals and intentions. Are you seeking relaxation, creative inspiration, or a deeper connection with yourself? By setting clear intentions, you can direct your cannabis experience towards a specific purpose, enhancing the desired aspect of your life.

2. **Mindful Consumption:** Practice mindful consumption by starting with lower doses and gradually increasing as needed. Pay attention to the cultivar's potency, cannabinoid profile, and terpene composition to choose one that aligns with your desired experience. Remember, it's not about how much you consume but rather the quality of your experience.

3. **Engage in Activities:** Instead of succumbing to couch-lock, engage in activities that stimulate your mind and body. Whether it's engaging in creative endeavors, enjoying nature, or participating in physical activities, cannabis can enhance the experience and add a new dimension of enjoyment. Be proactive and seek out experiences that align with your intentions rather than ones that will hinder them.

4. **Balance and Moderation:** Like all things in life, balance is key. Avoid excessive consumption that leads to inebriation and a loss of control. Pace yourself, listen to your body, and be mindful of your tolerance levels. By practicing moderation, you can maintain a harmonious relationship with cannabis and prevent negative stereotypes from taking hold.

Remember, being elevated is about embracing the positive aspects of cannabis and utilizing its potential to enhance various aspects of life. It's about tapping into creativity, finding inspiration, and connecting with oneself and others. By shifting our collective mindset, we can empower ourselves and redefine the narrative surrounding cannabis use.

So, my fellow cannabis connoisseurs, let's rise above the stereotypes and embrace a true essence of elevation. Let's showcase the multifaceted nature of cannabis and demonstrate that responsible consumption can lead to a more enriched, fulfilling, and productive life. It's time to shatter the stoner stereotype and elevate ourselves to new heights of understanding, appreciation and recognition.

11
SAFETY:
WHY REGULATED MARKETS EXIST

In this chapter, we're going to dive into the world of cannabis shopping and why turning to licensed dispensaries is the safest and most reliable option. We will also discuss the scary, yet for some reason popular, gas station gummies and the confusing sea of fake products we encounter in the real world each day.

Picture this: you stroll into a gas station or a head shop, eyes wide with anticipation, searching for that cannabis fix your buddy told you to look for. But let me tell you, my friend, the shelves of those establishments are like the lawless wasteland of cannabis products. You're taking a gamble, not just with your money, but with your health, body, mind and overall well-being.

Let's talk about those "gummies" you can buy at the corner store. Oh, the allure of those colorful packages and promises of a sweet, cannabis-infused experience – some may even bear the logos of popular cannabis brands. This must be legit, right? But let's be real here - those gummies are either total frauds or, if they do produce any high, it's likely due to a cocktail of lab-created chemicals that have more in common with a science experiment gone wrong than with actual cannabis. That packaging with the logo – yeah, it was likely purchased on an international wholesale website for pennies on the dollar and stuffed with whatever chemical cocktail the creators wished.

Now, don't get me wrong, I appreciate some good R&D or experimentation as much as the next curious mind. But when it comes to what we put in our bodies, it's best to stick with the real deal. That's where regulated dispensaries or retailers come in. These **licensed establishments** are the guardians of quality and consistency, ensuring that what you're consuming is genuine cannabis, not some mysterious concoction that raises more questions than it answers.

You see, when you buy from a licensed dispensary or retailer, you're not just getting a product; you're getting peace of mind. These businesses operate under strict regulations and undergo rigorous testing processes to ensure that what you're purchasing is safe, reliable, and true to its label. They work with reputable suppliers who adhere to standards that put some food regulations to shame

Think of regulated cannabis as the shield protecting you from the poisons and snake oils of the unregulated market. The local plug might have a charming smile a friendly demeanor and even a solid price, but can you trust what they're selling? Are they really putting your well-being first? It's like playing Russian roulette with a bong - one wrong move, and you could find yourself stating a giant *"what the fuck was that?"* on your exhale.

Joking aside, it is also important to recognize the seriousness of the issue. Your health, your safety, and your overall experience with cannabis matter. That's why it's crucial to choose the regulated path, to walk into licensed businesses with confidence, knowing that you're in good hands.

Leave the gas stations, head shops, and "local plugs" to their own devices. Opt for the safety net of regulated cannabis, where quality and consistency reign supreme. Because life is too short to gamble with your ganja or mind, folks.

12
UNDERSTANDING THE DISPENSARY

Whether a first-day employee or first-time visitor to a dispensary, it can be an overwhelming experience. There are so many out there, new ones developing overnight at times, all with their own unique aesthetics, workflows, staffing, and overall vibe. This chapter is aimed to help break down some key factors to consider when entering a dispensary, regardless of the market – if the dispensary is in a legal state, much of the following should apply.

1. **Dispensary Atmosphere** *(From Chill to Clinical)* Dispensaries come in various styles, ranging from cozy and welcoming to sleek and clinical. The atmosphere sets the tone for your experience, so pay attention to the dispensary's overall vibe. Some dispensaries have a lounge-like feel with comfortable seating and a laid-back ambiance, while others may adopt a more professional setting. Choose a dispensary that aligns with your preferences and makes you feel comfortable and at ease.

2. **Knowledgeable Staff** *(The Cannabis Connoisseurs)* One of the most valuable assets of a dispensary is its knowledgeable staff. Budtenders are there to assist you, answer questions, and provide guidance in selecting the right products for your needs. They should be well-versed in different cultivars, consumption methods, and product variations. Don't hesitate to ask for their recommendations or seek their expertise to enhance your dispensary experience.

3. **Product Selection** (*A Cornucopia of Cannabis*) Dispensaries offer a wide range of cannabis products to cater to various preferences and needs. From flower and concentrates to edibles and topicals, the options can be overwhelming. Take your time to explore the product selection, read labels, and ask questions about potency, ingredients, and consumption methods. Consider your desired effects, preferred consumption method, and any specific requirements you may have to make informed choices.

4. **Understanding The Names** (*Decoding the Cannabis Language*) Cultivar names can be perplexing, especially for newcomers. Familiarize yourself with common cultivar names and their characteristics to decipher the cannabis language. Indica cultivars are often associated with relaxation and sedation, while sativa cultivars are known for their energizing and uplifting effects. Hybrid cultivars offer a blend of both. Don't be afraid to ask the dispensary staff for explanations or recommendations based on your desired effects.

5. **Consumption Methods** (*Finding Your Preferred Route*) Cannabis can be consumed in various ways, and dispensaries often carry products designed for different consumption methods. From smoking and vaping to edibles and tinctures, each method offers a unique experience and onset time. Consider your preferences, lifestyle, and desired effects when selecting a consumption method. The dispensary staff can guide you in finding the right products based on your preferred route of consumption.

6. **Responsible Dosing** (*Start Low, Go Slow*) When it comes to cannabis, responsible dosing is key. Start with low doses, especially if you are a beginner or trying a new product. Cannabis affects individuals differently, and it's important to find the right dosage for your tolerance and desired experience. The dispensary staff can provide dosing recommendations based on the potency of the product and your personal preferences.

7. **Dispensary Etiquette** (*Respect, Peace and Courtesy*) When visiting a dispensary, it's essential to observe proper etiquette. Respect the rules and regulations of the establishment, such as age restrictions and consumption guidelines. Be patient and

considerate, especially during busy times. Avoid using your phone excessively or taking photos without permission. Remember, a positive and respectful attitude fosters a welcoming and enjoyable environment for everyone.

8. **Dispensary Operating Systems** *(From Seed-To-Sale)* Behind the scenes of a dispensary, there is a regulatory framework in place to ensure compliance and traceability of cannabis products. One example of a common operating system used by many legal cannabis markets is *METRC (Marijuana Enforcement Tracking Reporting Compliance)*. METRC is a comprehensive tracking system designed to monitor and regulate the cannabis industry. Systems such as this are becoming more utilized by companies across the nation.

METRC, and platforms like it, serve as crucial tools for regulatory agencies and dispensaries to maintain transparency and accountability throughout the supply chain. It tracks the movement of cannabis plants and products from cultivation facilities to manufacturing facilities, distribution centers, and ultimately, to the dispensary where it is sold to consumers. Aka: *"Seed-To-Sale"*

The regulatory ties of platforms like METRC are significant. It helps state and local governments enforce regulations, prevent diversion, and ensure that cannabis products are safe and compliant. Dispensaries are required to use these systems to record and report all relevant data, including plant inventory, harvest information, product transfers, sales, and waste disposal.

METRC operates on a barcode system, where each cannabis plant or product is assigned a unique identifier that can be scanned and tracked at each stage of its journey. This level of traceability provides regulators with the ability to track cannabis products back to their origins, ensuring that they are sourced from legal and licensed facilities.

For dispensaries, these seed-to-sale systems help to streamline compliance processes by automating inventory management, facilitating accurate record-keeping, and simplifying reporting requirements. It helps dispensaries stay compliant with state regulations, avoid penalties, and maintain the integrity of the seed-to-sale tracking system.

By utilizing METRC, dispensaries contribute to the overall goal of establishing a well-regulated cannabis industry that focuses on product safety first. It enhances transparency, prevents black market activities as discussed in the previous chapter, and ensures that consumers have access to safe and legal cannabis products.

It's important to note that while METRC is a widely used operating system in the cannabis industry, different legal markets may have variations in their tracking systems. Some states may have their own proprietary systems or use different third-party platforms with similar objectives. Regardless, any legal operator will be using such technology leaving us with peace of mind in what we are purchasing.

Understanding the role of seed-to-sale operating systems in the dispensary setting is essential for both employees and consumers alike. It underscores the commitment to compliance and regulatory standards, providing confidence that the products being sold are part of a regulated, legal, and transparent supply chain.

13
TIPS & TRICKS

Welcome to the final hoo-rah of this book. Figured that we can close on a simple note, leaving a sort of bread crumb trail highlighting where cannabis can take you (or go with you) next. As mentioned in previous chapters, cannabis should always aim to "ADD TO" your daily activities and not "TAKE YOU AWAY" from them. Here you will find a mix of fun, spiritual and ah-ha inspiring notes. Enjoy and happy trails, no matter where cannabis may take you!

1. **Rolling the Perfect Cross-Joint** (*Master the Art*) Rolling a cross-joint is like creating a masterpiece—a true feat of cannabis craftsmanship. To achieve this marvel, you'll need two rolling papers and a touch of finesse. Start by rolling a regular joint as the base, leaving a small gap near the top (pro-tip: you can use a pin to push the hole). Then, roll a smaller joint and carefully insert it through the gap, creating the cross shape. Seal the joints together, ensuring a smooth connection. Light it up, and let the magical cross-joint experience begin!

2. **The Ancient Art of Smoke Tricks** (*Blow Their Minds*) Impress your friends and become the talk of the smoke circle by mastering the art of smoke tricks. From classic smoke rings to the mystical dragon, these tricks add an extra touch of enchantment to your cannabis sessions. Practice techniques like French inhales, ghost inhales, and waterfall exhales. With a little practice and a lot of imagination, you'll become a smoke

sorcerer in no time.

3. **What to Do When You're Too Stoned** (*Ride the Wave*) We've all been there—the moment when you feel a bit too stoned and need to regain your balance. Fear not and relax! Take a deep breath and remember that this is just a temporary state. Find a comfortable space, sip some water, and embrace the experience. Engage in activities that ground you, such as listening to soothing music, watching a favorite show, or indulging in a tasty snack. Ride the wave and trust that it will pass, leaving you with tales of your cosmic journey.

4. **Do Not Mix Alcohol & Cannabis** (*Avoiding the Spins*) For those who may have walked this treacherous path, I'm sure the mere mention of the word *"spins"* triggers an unsavory memory or two. Mixing alcohol and cannabis can be a recipe for an unpleasant experience that leaves you feeling dizzy, nauseous, and utterly disoriented for numerous reasons. So, let's be wise and keep these two troublemakers apart. We'll savor our cannabis and raise a glass of our favorite libation separately, enjoying their unique charms without risking a one-way ticket to the land of spins and regrets.

5. **High-Enhancing Activities** (*Elevate the Experience*) Cannabis has a knack for enhancing various activities, turning them into extraordinary adventures. Engage in creative pursuits such as painting, writing, or playing a musical instrument. Dive into the depths of nature with a hike or a leisurely stroll in a park. Immerse yourself in mind-bending movies or engage in stimulating conversations that open up new dimensions of thought. With cannabis as your guide, ordinary activities transform into extraordinary escapades.

6. **The Art of Cannabis Pairing** (*Flavors and Aromas*) Just like fine wine and gourmet meals, cannabis can be paired with complementary flavors and aromas. Experiment with different cultivars and explore their unique terpene profiles. Enhance your experience by pairing cultivars with foods, beverages, or even music that complement their flavors. Discover the symphony of sensations that arises when cannabis and complementary elements harmonize.

7. **The Traveler's Guide** (*Cannabis Adventures Await*) When embarking on cannabis-infused travels, it's essential to

understand local laws and regulations. Research cannabis-friendly destinations and explore the vibrant cannabis communities that exist worldwide. From cannabis-friendly accommodations to guided tours, the options for cannabis adventures are expanding. So pack your bags, venture forth, and let cannabis be your guide to unforgettable journeys. Cultivar Research: Knowledge is Power Before making a cannabis purchase, arm yourself with knowledge about different cultivars. Research the effects, flavors, and potential benefits of various cultivars to make an informed decision. Websites, online forums, and reputable cannabis publications can provide valuable insights and cultivar recommendations. Remember, knowledge is power when it comes to finding the perfect cultivar for your desired experience.

8. **Check THC and Cannabinoid Levels** (*Finding Your Balance*) Pay attention to the THC and cannabinoids levels listed on product labels. THC is responsible for the psychoactive effects of cannabis, while CBD and other cannabinoids offer potential therapeutic benefits without the high. Finding the right balance of THC and the other cannabinoids found in cannabis can help tailor your experience to your preferences and desired effects. Experiment with different ratios to discover what works best for you.

9. **Consider Terpene Profiles** (*Unleash Flavor and Aroma*) Don't overlook the importance of terpenes in your purchasing decisions. Terpenes are aromatic compounds found in cannabis that contribute to its flavor, aroma, and potential effects. Different terpenes can produce various experiences, from uplifting and energetic to relaxing and sedating. Look for products that disclose their terpene profiles, allowing you to choose cultivars with specific flavors and aromas that resonate with your preferences.

10. **Start with Low Dosages** (*The Art of Gradual Exploration*) If you're new to cannabis or trying a new product, start with low dosages. This approach allows you to gauge your sensitivity and tolerance to cannabis without becoming overwhelmed. Gradually increase your dosage over time as you become more familiar with its effects. Remember, it's easier to consume more if needed than to undo the effects of

consuming too much.

11. **Seek Recommendations** *(Tap into Collective Wisdom)* Tap into the collective wisdom of budtenders, friends, and fellow cannabis enthusiasts. Ask for recommendations based on your desired experience, preferences, and any specific needs you may have. Experienced budtenders can provide valuable guidance and insights, helping you navigate the vast array of products available. Sharing recommendations with others fosters a sense of community and helps build a shared knowledge base.

12. **Quality Matters** *(Seek Trusted Brands)* When making purchasing decisions, prioritize quality. Look for products from trusted brands that prioritize transparency, rigorous testing, and responsible cultivation practices. Trusted brands often provide detailed information about their cultivation methods, testing results, and sourcing. This ensures you're getting a safe and reliable product that meets the highest standards.

13. **Read Reviews and Feedback** *(Learn from Others' Experiences)* Take advantage of online reviews and feedback from other consumers. Platforms and websites dedicated to cannabis reviews can offer insights into specific cultivars, products, and brands. While everyone's experience is subjective, reading reviews can help you gather a broader understanding of a particular product's quality, effects, and overall reputation.

14. **DIY Cannabis Infusions** *(Become a Culinary Alchemist)* Unleash your inner culinary alchemist by creating your own cannabis-infused delights. Experiment with homemade infusions such as cannabis-infused butter (cannabutter) or oils. These versatile ingredients can be used in a variety of recipes, from sweet treats like brownies and cookies to savory dishes like pasta or stir-fries. Let your creativity soar as you transform everyday meals into extraordinary cannabis-infused masterpieces.

15. **Enhancing Sensuality** *(Cannabis and Intimacy)* Explore the realm of sensuality and intimacy with the help of cannabis. Cannabis can heighten sensations, deepen connections, and enhance pleasure. Incorporate cannabis into your intimate

moments through products like cannabis-infused lubricants or sensual massage oils. Discover a new level of intimacy and explore the vast potential of cannabis as an enhancer of pleasure and connection.

16. **<u>Cannabis and Meditation</u>** (*A Journey Within*) Combine the calming effects of cannabis with the practice of meditation to embark on a profound inner journey. Cannabis can help quiet the mind, deepen relaxation, and foster a greater sense of introspection. Create a peaceful setting, take a hit or consume a cannabis edible, and settle into a comfortable meditation posture. Allow cannabis to be your ally as you explore the depths of your consciousness and cultivate mindfulness.

14
A CLOSING NOTE

So we meet here in the final pages of the book, congratulations on making it through! Hopefully our little journey down the cannabis rabbit hole was of benefit and enjoyment. Beyond anything else, I hope it helps to grant a new level of understanding and respect for the plant, industry and culture behind it all. The shift begins with removing any prejudices or fears by looking at things through a sensible lens. Legal cannabis does not need to be the big scary monster that some make it out to be.

We are living in a progressive, fast-moving world and cannabis is no stranger to the concept. The momentum that this industry has gained in such short time is something of wonder and more importantly, is something to stay ahead of. It's absurd to think that we are smack dab in the middle of a modern cannabis revolution and baseline educational material is still so absent and inaccessible for most.

The public has been kept in the dark for too long with both research and education still lacking in a major way. That brings us back to the main purpose of this book, to shed light on the topic in a relatable way and ultimately support a positive public perception of the industry as it continues to gain momentum.

In lieu of federal legislation at this stage, we find ourselves in a bind. The bind of needing legitimate research and information yet being refused as an industry due to laws, restrictions & flat out fear. To break down the sheer silliness of how things are currently set up would take another book in itself. To summarize: how are people utilizing a plant so multifaceted and beneficial to wellness yet it sits in the same category as heroin? Thought provoking to say the least.

All we can do is continue to share facts rather than spread fear. And that my friends, is why we are here after all. As you close this book to place on the shelf, a cheers in order. Grab your stash, get your pipe, vape, joint or whatever apparatus you choose and light it up. For you are now among the growing number of elevated minds whom recognize cannabis as the wellness-wonder that it is while choosing to take a sturdy stance behind it.

As this industry continues to grow and change over time, so may this book. It would be an injustice to let the content gather dust and neglect proper updating. With growing support on a global scale, new and exciting updates are coming about constantly within this realm. Stay tuned and surely keep an open mind, as we are likely in for quite the ride over the next few decades. Further, hold on to this copy as it may act as an interesting snapshot of cannabis during the early days of legalization. It will be something to look back on, learn from and ultimately build upon.

Until we cross paths again,

Joe

©Joseph Kozlowski 2023

INDEX PAGE

ABOUT THE AUTHOR

Joseph is a compelling author and esteemed figure in the realm of alternative medicine. His unwavering focus on cannabis stems from a deeply personal experience, witnessing its transformative therapeutic potential for his own family members battling various ailments and enduring the arduous journey of recovery. This encounter sparked an unyielding passion and commitment, propelling him to champion the ongoing progress of cannabis legalization and spearhead support in normalizing the plant.

From orchestrating grassroots campaigns at the very footsteps of our government to overseeing expansive cannabis operations on a multiple-state level, Joseph's path has been crystal clear. Now, with his first book, he seeks to extend his profound passion and share the invaluable wisdom gained throughout his remarkable journey with a wider audience.

Made in the USA
Las Vegas, NV
25 January 2024

84859528R10049